OBSERVATIONS AND EXPERIMENTS IN NATURAL HISTORY

ALAN DALE

Observations
and Experiments in
Natural History

HEINEMANN
LONDON MELBOURNE TORONTO

First published 1960
© Alan Dale, 1960

Published by
William Heinemann Ltd
15–16 Queen Street, London, W.1
Printed in Great Britain by Butler & Tanner Ltd
Frome and London

PREFACE

THESE DAYS there are available many books dealing with nature study and ecology, but this book, though concerned with some aspects of natural history, is rather different. I have covered a wide field of plants and animals, because, unlike the specialists who are said to ' know more and more about less and less ', I have preferred to know ' less and less about more and more ' and have enjoyed all the many aspects of natural history that have come my way.

True, when I was younger I went through the collecting phase. I think that the making of collections is an excellent foundation for future biologists. I myself collected flowering plants and ferns as a matter of course; butterflies and moths for a spell, then ants, followed by beetles and molluscs. Mosses were rather difficult to name until E. V. Watson's book *British Mosses* was published, but since then they have given me much pleasure. I shall not continue my list, but only say that I think I learned most biology from collecting beetles, though even collecting galls or leaf miners (see pp. 65 *et seq.*) may take one into the deeper mysteries of biology. It may be preferable for you to make a collection of the plants and animals from a definite habitat, such as a roadside, wood or a stretch of water; but there will inevitably be many plants (e.g. fungi) and animals (e.g. two-winged flies and small wasps) which you cannot name.

It is my hope that this book will appeal to many young scientists—not only those intending to be biologists—because I have stressed the importance of both observation and experiment—the essential processes for anyone intent on a scientific career. The book is a mixture of the two. Essentially it is based on a series of notes which, for the most part, I made in Staffordshire during 1948 and 1949. I have preferred to retain the note style of presentation even though it sacrifices a certain amount of continuity, but since the book is intended to be a stimulus-book and not a treatise or text-book on natural history, I feel that continuity is not essential.

My notes were varied. Some, such as that on bees visiting white dead nettle flowers from which the petals had fallen (p. 140), were matters of pure observation. Other notes concerned little experiments which I carried out myself, such as the experiment concerning the regeneration of earthworms cut into two parts (p. 25). I have added to these some experiments which my pupils have done, e.g. the analysis of the weeds in the lawn and its comparison with the plant analysis of a nearby grazing meadow. There are also a very few experiments I have not personally carried out, but have included because of their intrinsic value. I have not hesitated to insert broad or detailed biological facts where these seemed appropriate.

Two gentlemen, Messrs. L. C. Comber and A. H. Short, gave me the benefit of their constructive criticism and have in this way been responsible for considerable improvements. I thank them sincerely. I should also like to thank Messrs. E. L. Greenwood and Bob Straughan for reading the proofs. Finally, I must thank those members of my publishers' staff who have dealt with the various aspects of the book's production, and in particular Alan Hill who guided and cheered me at a time when I was recovering from a serious operation.

ALAN DALE

January, 1960

CONTENTS

LIST OF PLATES

CHAPTER ONE

INTRODUCTION

OBSERVATIONS

OBSERVATIONS ARE usually not too difficult to make since it is merely a matter of using your sense organs, mainly the eyes; although in some instances the ears, nose, pain, touch, or other organs may be required to make an observation either as well as, or instead of, the eyes.

You must be as certain as you can that your observation is accurate. You must make assurance doubly sure. It is very easy to get a faulty impression of an event, as so frequently is shown by witnesses of a street accident when questioned by the police. Professor Beveridge, in his book *The Art of Scientific Investigation*, gives a very succinct example:

' " We are prone to see what lies behind our eyes rather than what appears before them," an old saying goes. An illustration of this is seen in the cinema film depicting a lion pursuing a negro. The camera shows now the lion pursuing, now the man fleeing, and after several repetitions of this we finally see the lion leap on something in the long grass. Even though the lion and the man have at no time appeared on the screen together, most people in the audience are convinced they actually saw the lion leap on the man, and there have been serious protests that natives were sacrificed to make such a film.'

There are some observations which can be made only at certain times. For instance, if you had a single butterfly chrysalis, and wished to observe the emergence of the butterfly, you would have to keep the chrysalis under constant observation. But constant observation is impossible for you if you lead an active life. However, if you obtain 50, or better still 100, chrysalides, you can inspect their cage once a day until you see some butterflies have emerged; you *then* commence your observation of emergence by waiting. You can make chance observations on a variety of phenomena during your daily life, and especially on country walks, though towns also have much to offer if you are alert for opportunities. Liverworts in a street in Derby, fern prothalli in Coventry, and a black-throated diver on the river at Bakewell are three examples of my own observations in town streets. The mosses *Tortula muralis* can often be found on roofs and walls, and the silvery moss *Bryum argenteum* grows even on some station platforms.

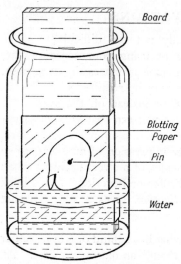

FIG. 1.—One method of growing a broad-bean seedling.

A different aspect of observation is that you may make a single observation on an individual plant or animal and *you* may be certain it is a true one. However, Science will not accept it as a *fact* until the same observation is made by other observers. Neither may you assume that all the other members of this species will yield the same observation, because living things are never completely alike—not even identical twins. I had an excellent example of this quite recently. I was growing a broad-bean seed on blotting paper, which surrounded a piece of board standing vertically in a jam-jar (Fig. 1). In the jar was just sufficient water to immerse the hilum (the black scar) on the broad bean. The bean germinated and the root grew downwards, as I expected the main root of a bean should. One day I saw that the tip of the root was turning towards the horizontal. Then it began to grow vertically upwards, and ultimately made a complete loop (Plate I, A). Now, I have never seen this happen before, and it is not characteristic of broad beans in general; but I should have thought that it was, if this had been my only observation on germinating broad beans.

It is essential that a scientist should not base conclusions on a single observation, nor even on a few observations. The more observations of a natural history object or process, the more likely is the eventual conclusion to be valid, for an organism may change its reaction from one observation to another.

Once I was walking across fields in Shropshire to a river which, because of a rise in the ground, I could not see. Suddenly a wild scream pierced the evening air. I was startled, and ran to the top of the bank so that I could see the river. As I stood watching, a baby rabbit, perhaps three weeks old, came and settled on my shoes, shivering with fright. Then I saw what I took to be the mother rabbit fighting with a stoat, and as I looked she kicked it into the river with a powerful blow from her back legs.

As a result of this rousing observation, I *could* say that rabbits can defeat stoats in battle; and that wild baby rabbits come to man for protection. But wild baby rabbits run away from men as a rule, and stoats kill adult rabbits as a rule. My observation was of an exceptional case, and is a warning to be sure in your observations until you are doubly sure. Also, I was not certain that the adult rabbit was the mother of the little one, or even related to it.

These four points of observation are perhaps worth repeating, briefly:

(1) One, or more, of the sense organs may be required for a particular observation (e.g., it may not be until it sings that you can recognise a bird in a wood).

(2) Some observations must be made at particular times, (e.g. spider making web, newts mating).

(3) Because an observation has been made on a particular organism, it is not correct to assume that all the members of the species will yield the same observation, e.g. one may sometimes see an apple tree in flower in late summer, but not all apple trees of the same variety flower in this way.

(4) As many observations as possible should be made of a particular event (e.g. the density of weeds on a lawn, p. 130).

EXPERIMENTS

Experiments are rather different from observations because an experiment must have a question to answer. For instance, I had a doe and a buck rabbit. I mated them together, but the doe failed to have a litter. I mated them again, and once more the doe failed to produce a litter. This happened a third time. So far, it was simply a matter of observation. But now I asked myself the question, ' Is my doe sterile? ' Well, the obvious experiment here is to mate her with another buck known to be the father of litters with other does. I did this, and my doe produced a fine litter of chinchillas. This result meant that the answer to my question ' Is the doe sterile? ' was ' No '. This immediately raised the question, ' Is the buck sterile? ' I did not test him by mating him to another doe, but if he had proved fertile I should have had to assume that both rabbits were fertile, but that they were incompatible with each other.

Biological experiments should have five main parts, viz.
(1) A question to answer.
(2) A hypothesis (that is, a kind of informed guess based on known facts).
(3) A method to test the hypothesis. Very often the method must have a control (p. 6).
(4) A result to the test of the hypothesis.
(5) A conclusion which will answer the question.

Usually a negative result is not much use. As an example of this let me tell you of a perfectly good experiment my wife made when she was five years old. She had a question to answer: ' Where does the water go when you pull the lavatory chain ? ' From time to time she had seen water flush down an outside grid underneath the lavatory, which was on the first floor, and she made her hypothesis ' I bet it goes down the drain '.

She now devised an ingenious method of testing this hypothesis. It was to take some small sticks which had been chopped to light the fire, and put them in the lavatory pan. Then she pulled the chain and rushed to the grid outside. She had expected to see the sticks caught on the grating—but none were there. The result of her experiment was negative, and proved that her hypothesis was not correct; the sticks did not come out in the water going down the grid. Consequently, her young mind had to accept the conclusion that she had not obtained an answer to her original question (though she would not have thought like this). Fortunately (or unfortunately) the sticks blocked the sewage pipe and a plumber had to be called. He found the sticks, and so obtained a positive result which provided the answer to the question.

The experiment described does show that a negative conclusion can be drawn, though with less certainty by far than that from a positive result.   In this case, the conclusion to be drawn before the plumber comes is that *either* the water goes some other way *or* the water went down the drain but the sticks could not get that far.   Very often research workers have to spend a lot of time proving that the sticks could have got all the way, if the water went that way.   You see, in biological things, you can't call in the plumber.

Biological experiments are not always easy or simple to carry out, for there are usually several factors to consider. There may be factors operating of which the experimenter has no knowledge, as in the case of the supposedly mathematically intelligent horse ' Clever Hans ', who could do remarkable sums his trainer set on a blackboard in front of him.

For a long time this ability was a great mystery, although serious scientists could not accept the idea that a horse could do maths.   Finally it was discovered that the horse could not count without his trainer.   In fact the horse was watching the trainer, who counted the number of hoof taps and unconsciously relaxed his tension when the horse had given the correct number.   The trainer's attention to the hoof taps was the critical factor.   Remove him (or replace him) and the horse was bewildered.   I should add that the trainer was quite honest in this matter.

To overcome this difficulty of unsuspected factors, biologists use the principle of a *Control* in the method part of their experiments.   That means that when they have a question to investigate they first make their hypothesis and then devise a method of testing it.   To do this they set up a *Control experiment* in which all known factors are present (or, more strictly, it is an experiment which works; you cannot be certain that you have all the relevant factors present). Then they set up other experiments in which *a single factor* is missing. The control results act as a standard against which the experimental results are checked. If the control does not work, the whole experiment is a failure. Provided that the control works satisfactorily according to your expectations, the results from the experimental ' set-ups ' should give a conclusion which answers the original question. If they do not, it means that vital factors have not been considered, and in fact this frequently happens in biological experiments. An experiment illustrating the use of a *Control* is that concerned with the regeneration of worms (p. 25).

As an example I shall quote an experiment on broad beans on which I was engaged for several months. I was anxious to obtain a photograph of a bean growing on a board (as in Fig. 1), and I soaked some beans in tap water for 36 hours. Many of the radicles were about to burst through the seed skin (*testa*), and I chose six beans, placing two (one on each side of the board) in each pot, with water coming up to the hilum.

I have germinated and grown beans in this manner many times, and usually most of the seeds germinate. First their roots grow down into the water and later the shoot is withdrawn from between the cotyledons inside the testa. I was very surprised, therefore, when on this occasion the roots, after growing between $\frac{1}{4}$ in. and $\frac{1}{2}$ in., ceased to elongate, and in fact grew no more. The growing tips became mucilaginous and some were nearly black at the extreme end.

I was faced with the question ' Why do my beans not grow ? ' Then I remembered that the boards were cut from the side of an unwanted beehive, and had been covered with white paint on one side. I had planed the actual paint off, but I thought, ' Clearly the growth has stopped because of chemicals from the paint', remembering vaguely that white-lead paint is poisonous. Therefore I was able to make an ' informed guess ' (my hypothesis) that some of the chemicals had penetrated the wood and were poisoning the beans, either by direct contact or by solution in the water. My method of testing my hypothesis was merely to soak more beans and mount them in fresh water on new pieces of wood which had not been painted. The result was the same as before—the beans stopped growing. The conclusion was that it was *not* the painting of the wood which caused lack of growth.

Then I recalled how, many years earlier, in a different part of the country, I had failed year after year to demonstrate that a clay suspension in water will not settle quickly until lime water is added to it. Unfortunately my control jar of clay suspension in tap water, without lime water, always settled just as quickly (I suppose my pupils thought ' Why doesn't he fiddle it ? '). After some years a thought occurred to me: ' The tap water here is hard—it probably contains chemicals which will agglutinate[1] a clay suspension.' At once I made a suspension in distilled water, and the suspension remained long after the one treated with lime water had settled and become clear.

Remembering this, I made a new hypothesis for my beans—that their growth was arrested because of some substance in the tap water. My method now was merely to germinate and grow them in rain water, which I collected in a well-washed bucket and a bowl. Alas, I still got a negative result. Changing the water made no difference.

Then one day a friend called in, and I told him of my

[1] Agglutinate means cause the suspended clay particles to clump together to make larger units which soon sink to the bottom.

failure. He was interested and made three suggestions, viz. the factors inhibiting growth could be one of the following:

(1) Insufficient oxygen in the water. I myself thought this to be unlikely, since beans had always grown well enough before, when I had never changed the water.

(2) Too great a difference in the temperature when I added fresh water. I had not thought of that. The difference was about 15° F.

(3) The seeds were contaminated with bacteria or fungi: most likely bacteria. This possibility had not occurred to me, either.

These suggestions made me decide upon a full-scale experiment, but at this stage we changed our residence from Bakewell to Borrowash near Derby. Also, I found I had only four beans left. They were beans purchased in 1957, and I could not obtain any more. In fact I was unable to purchase new beans until the end of October, and these were a much lighter brown than the four old ones, being 1958 crop.

I placed the four old beans in tap-water in a dish, and similarly four of the new beans. To speed germination I placed them in our fire oven, which is usually warm but not hot. All the beans germinated. The water containing the new season's beans remained clear, but the water with the four old beans soon became cloudy, which made me suspect bacterial activity. However, since the beans were germinating, I pinned them out on boards as before, but this time I sterilised the jam-jars and boards by heating them in a pressure cooker.

After a few days I changed the water in two of the 'new bean' pots and two of the 'old bean' pots for well-oxygenated water, leaving the others unchanged. I repeated the water changes after another three days. The results are

B

shown in Fig. 2. The most remarkable were old bean No. 7, which grew well, and new bean No. 1, growing in two changes of oxygenated water; for *after* each change the root grew horizontally for a while, but then became vertical,

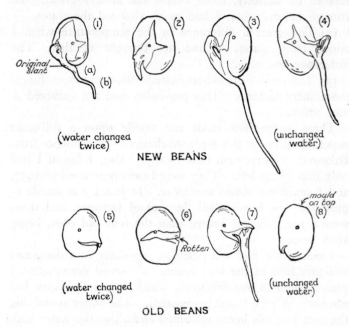

FIG. 2.—Drawings of the new and old beans, the germination of which is discussed in the text.

so as to give the step formation shown in the picture. Its companion No. 2 ceased to grow after a few days and the radicle developed a black mucilaginous tip. Nos. 3 and 4, which were kept in the original water, grew quite well, at least suggesting that sufficient oxygen for growth entered from the air. Of the old beans, Nos. 5, 6 and 8 ceased to grow; but I have mentioned that No. 7 grew well in two changes of oxygenated water.

I was now greatly intrigued; but I still had not found the answer to my question, nor had I any more of the old beans. Suddenly I wondered why No. 2 should have started to grow and then stop. I thought about it a good deal before I realised that I had used an old pin to fix it to the board, a pin which had been used on one of the ' old ' beans that had ceased to grow. This aroused my suspicion that some harmful bacteria or fungi had been transferred on this pin. When in a few days the bean went black around the pinhole, the suspicion was strengthened. The patch had a diameter of about $\frac{1}{2}$ in. on the outer side of the bean, and about $\frac{3}{4}$ in. on the inside. The blotting paper against and below the bean was very mucilaginous.

In the absence of any more old beans, and in the light of my experience, I decided to do another experiment. This time the question was, ' What is the effect of (a) tap water, and (b) changing the water of beans germinating at 65° F. to cooler water, 50° F. ? ' The hypothesis was ' at least some beans will have their growth affected by these factors '.

The experiment was set up as follows:

The beans were soaked in distilled water in a porridge plate for 36 hours. By then all were germinating visibly. I had carried this out on the mantelpiece where the temperature of water came within a degree or so of 65° F. This time I sterilised the jam-pots, the pins and the pieces of wood with their blotting paper fastened to them by drawing pins. I arranged the pots as follows:

(1) *Control.* Two germinating seeds, pinned as before —one on either side of the board and just touching distilled water in the bottom of the jar. In this control I changed the oxygenated distilled water twice—the new water having the same temperature as the old.

(2) *Experimental I.*   Two seeds in distilled water.   Two changes of distilled water 15° F. lower in temperature than the jar water.

(3) *Experimental II.*   Two seeds in tap water (remember all seeds were germinated in distilled water).   Tap water changed twice at the same temperature.

(4) *Experimental III.*   Two seeds in tap water.   Water changed twice, the fresh water being 15° F. cooler.

No special oxygenation was carried out on the water of any of the experimental pots.

The result was that all the seeds grew well, those in the control and also those in the experimental jars.   The conclusion, you will see, must be that these factors do *not* interfere with broad-bean seeds germinating normally, and this is a negative conclusion since it does not answer the original question, ' Why do my (old) beans not grow ? '   A great and obvious weakness of the various experiments is that in each case only two beans were used to be subjected to the various conditions.   Look again at Fig. 2, No. 7.   One hundred beans used in each of the experiments might have given quite different results and conclusions.   Because I had no more of the beans, I could not confirm my suspicions that the cause of my old beans failing to continue to grow after germination was due to bacterial infection; but looking at the whole set of experiments (and especially the part played by unsterilised pins), bacterial infection seems to me to be the most likely cause.   It will be easy to test this hypothesis if ever I come across more beans which behave in a similar manner.

CHAPTER TWO

INVERTEBRATE ANIMALS, EXCLUDING INSECTS

IF YOU run your hand down the back of your neck or along the midline of your back, you will be able to feel the structure we call the backbone. You should be able to verify that it is made of a number of separate bones, called vertebrae. Each vertebra has a hole running through it from the head end to the tail end, and through this canal the main trunk line of the nervous system, the spinal cord, passes from the brain.

All animals which possess such a spinal column are said to belong to the group of VERTEBRATES, even though in some fishes there is no bone, but another supporting tissue called cartilage. Cartilage you will know as the supporting tissue of your ear flaps. In the lung fishes (the *Dipnoi*) there are no separate vertebrae. The vertebrates are divided into five classes, the fishes, the amphibians, the reptiles, the birds, and the mammals. All the other animals we shall meet in this book have no vertebral column and are called INVERTEBRATES. In this present chapter I shall mention a variety of invertebrates; but insects, which are also invertebrates, will be reserved for Chapter III. Experiments and observations on vertebrates will be found in Chapter IV.

HYDRA

One of the invertebrates that I always find fascinating is the tiny green hydra (*Hydra viridis*) which occurs on the weeds of most stretches of still water. Quite small areas will yield hydras. I know a small well, not more than two yards by one yard in area, and having only a few clumps of water moss (*Fontinalis antipyretica*) as a weed, and yet it yields hydras year after year. A few miles away is a disused limestone quarry, where a tiny pond no bigger than an average table has formed on the rock at the foot of the worked face. This, too, yields hydras in profusion.

In the warmer months of the year it should be possible to obtain hydras by putting water weeds from several ponds or lakes in separate jam-pots, and if possible filling the jars up to the neck with water from where the plants were collected. If enough of this water is not available use rain water instead. The duckweed floating at the surface of ponds is said to yield hydras abundantly, but this has not been my experience.

In a day or two, if hydras are present, some will be found attached to the glass walls of the jam-jars, and others on the plants should easily be picked out. They are green (grass-green, one might say) in colour, and the body is cylindrical in shape (Fig. 3). The base of the cylinder adheres tenaciously to the sub-stratum, being glued onto it by a secretion from the basal cells. There is no opening in the basal disc. The other end has a circlet of tentacles which surround the mouth and can project freely into the water. Hydras are quite small but are capable of contracting or expanding. When contracted, an average hydra may be about 1 mm. long, but when fully expanded it may measure 2 cm. or more, though both the body and the tentacles are then very thin. It is quite easy to make an expanded hydra contract, usually by merely knocking the container, or approaching it in the water with a pencil. Watch them to see if they contract occasionally without any outside stimulation. The hydras may be transferred from one vessel to another by a small glass pipette with a rubber teat (the device sold as a 'dropper' by chemists for a few pence).

It is instructive to watch hydras feeding. They live mainly on small aquatic creatures such as *Daphnia*, *Cyclops* and ostracods, which are all crustaceans; but I have seen

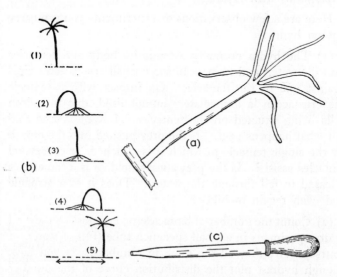

FIG. 3.—(*a*) *Hydra* animal expanded in water, × 20; (*b*) diagrams which show one method of moving from place to place by *Hydra*; (*c*) glass pipette for catching small aquatic organisms.

photographs of a hydra eating a small fish, and presumably they would tackle other small water creatures, mainly insect larvae. This you could investigate by putting hydras into a jam-pot containing small gnat or mosquito larvae, which can often be found abundantly in the marginal water of small ponds. Small tanks of water (even buckets will do), when left full of water, with soil at the bottom, frequently attract gnats and mosquitoes to lay their eggs there. I remember very well as a boy being mystified by the curious 'wrigglers' which appeared year after year in our cottage rain-tub—which must have contained rotting leaves blown into it each autumn.

Experiments with Hydra

Here are a few observations or experiments you can carry out on hydra:

(1) The hydra normally extends its body and tentacles into the water, and waits until some small crustacean swims against one of the tentacles. On impact with a tentacle the crustacean is immediately immobilised, due to poison cells being situated on the tentacles. I want you to find out what happens next. Is the prey pushed into the mouth by the single tentacle to which it is attached, or do several tentacles assist? Is the prey always held, or is it sometimes released to fall through the water? Does it ever struggle and even regain mobility?

(2) Count the number of tentacles (no easy task) on several hydra specimens in a small specimen tube (full of water, of course). Are they all the same in number? If you have enough hydras, plot the distribution curve of the number of tentacles against the number of individuals, and so find the average number of tentacles. You may possibly find it easier to count the tentacles if you transfer the hydras to a white saucer. You will need a hand lens to be accurate in your count.

(3) Cut several hydras into two parts by a transverse cut, and allow each pair of parts to regenerate in pond water in a glass specimen tube. You need a separate tube for each pair of hydra parts. Do both parts have the same number of tentacles when regeneration is complete? Is this so in all cases?

(4) Find out if the buds on hydra always have the same number of tentacles as the parent.

(5) Place a flourishing colony of hydras in a jam-pot nearly full of water. Then put on the jam-pot a cover made of black paper (or of several thicknesses of brown) so that the pot is entirely closed except for a window half an inch square on one side, cut through the paper cover. After a few days remove the cover and find out if the distribution of the hydras bears any definite relation to the window—really, of course, to the beam of light passing through the window. You will find it useful, using Indian ink, to trace the outline of the window frame onto the outside of the pot, before removing the cover.

Repeat with a stock of white *Hydra* if you can catch these not so common animals. If there is a difference in behaviour between the white and green *Hydra*, suggest a reason for it.

(6) It is well worthwhile to make an attempt to see a hydra move from one place to another. They do this more frequently than one might expect, especially if there is little food available. Using a dropper, squirt half a dozen hydras in water into a specimen tube, or even into a watch glass. Have this colony where you can watch it from time to time, using a hand lens. You are fairly certain, sooner or later, to see a hydra balance on its tentacles and then bring the body right over the tentacles so that the basal disc may find on the other side of the body a new place to anchor. In this way the animal moves slowly along to a new location. There is said to be another way of locomotion where the body moves along in a series of loops. Look out for this also.

OSTRACODS, *DAPHNIA* AND *CYCLOPS*

In all unpolluted ponds, lakes and stagnant ditches is found a great variety of crustaceans, of which the ostracods, *Daphnia* and *Cyclops* are extremely common.   They

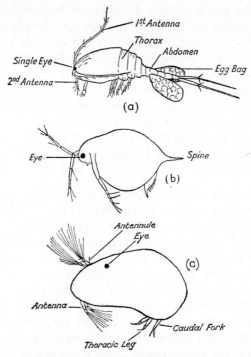

Fig. 4.—(*a*) *Cyclops*; (*b*) young *Daphnia*; (*c*) an ostracod.
All ×15.

are all quite tiny but they should easily be recognised from Fig. 4.   These creatures, and others of similar size, are among the main scavengers of water in which leaves and stems of various plants are rotting through the action of various bacteria, fungi and protozoans. The small creatures mentioned above are themselves food for larger creatures which are carnivorous, and since *Hydra* is one such carnivore it can be fed on a culture of small crustaceans and will grow rapidly in numbers, splitting off many *Hydra*.

A culture of ostracods, *Daphnia* and similar creatures can be made very simply, merely by scraping a jam-pot along the floor of a pond, so that plenty of the rotting detritus there is collected in the jam-pot, which will now be fairly full of water. Add a few of last autumn's fallen leaves, and stand the pot in a darkish place for about two months. At the end of this time it should be teeming with tiny life. Of course, in preparing the culture, remove any of the larger creatures which happen to be present. Such things as damsel fly larvae, or beetle larvae, may have been collected during the scooping process; as they grow they will be quite easy to remove, even if too tiny to spot at first.

Of course, after April, you can catch very many of these smaller organisms in a plankton-net[1]—but raising a culture is more fun.

FLUKE LARVAE FROM THE COMMON POND SNAIL (*Limnaea stagnalis*)

One day I had been collecting in a lake near Coventry, and immediately after reaching home I decided to put the animals I had caught into separate containers. By luck I had not enough jars, and I was compelled to put a common pond snail in a 3 in. × 1 in. flat-bottomed collector's tube, as I wanted the snail on my desk. I half filled the tube with pond water.

I did not look at the pond snail until the following morning, and then to my astonishment the snail was in what

---

[1] A fine-mesh net.

appeared to be a very dilute milk solution. I decided to look at the liquid at once through a microscope. I placed a drop of the ' milk ' solution on a microscope slide, slipped a cover glass over, and set it on the microscope stage. When brought into focus, the ' milk ' explained itself at once, for countless numbers of cercariae of some fluke or other wriggled incessantly in the fluid. They looked most bizarre, with a sucker at the front and a larger sucker at about the middle of the body, in between the arms of a horseshoe-shaped intestine. It was all very clear. As they forged through the fluid the cercariae went through curious movements, developing a pronounced waist, the constriction then passing along to the front of the body and disappearing (Fig. 5).

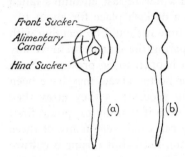

FIG. 5.—A fluke cercaria which emerged from a common pond snail.

Almost every specimen of fresh-water mollusc (including the fresh-water mussel) is likely to contain fluke larvae, and these may often be revealed by dissection of the mollusc in clear water. A good hand lens will be necessary, as in so many biological investigations. Some flukes occur as ecto-parasites on the gills of fishes. Another group of flukes are endo-parasites and may have as many as three hosts in their life cycle—for example, the fluke which produces, in the fresh-water mussel, cercariae which swim away to encyst in the mouth of the roach. There they wait until the roach is eaten by a perch, and in this third host the cercariae develop into flukes.

To explain exactly what a cercaria is, I shall outline the

life history of the fluke (*Fasciola hepatica*) found in the liver of sheep. It has a life cycle characteristic of many flukes.

The sheep fluke is about 1 in. long, and flat like a leaf (see

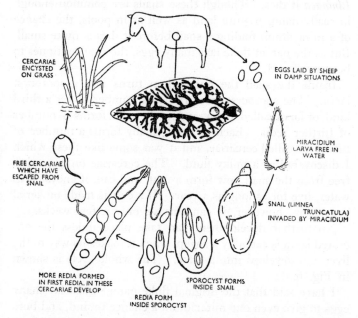

CERCARIAE
ENCYSTED
ON GRASS

EGGS LAID BY SHEEP
IN DAMP SITUATIONS

MIRACIDIUM
LARVA FREE IN
WATER

FREE CERCARIAE
WHICH HAVE
ESCAPED FROM
SNAIL

SNAIL (LIMNEA
TRUNCATULA)
INVADED BY MIRACIDIUM

MORE REDIA FORMED
IN FIRST REDIA. IN THESE
CERCARIAE DEVELOP

SPOROCYST FORMS
INSIDE SNAIL

REDIA FORM
INSIDE SPOROCYST

FIG. 6.—Diagram of the life cycle of the liver fluke. In the centre is a life-size drawing of the adult on which two suckers and the branched food canal are shown. The larval stages are not drawn to scale. As with most internal parasites, the egg is small. The chances are increased in the liver fluke by the reproduction which goes on in the sporocyst and redia stages, so that from each egg a large number of cercariae is ultimately produced.

Fig. 6). The developing eggs are passed down the bile duct into the intestine and so out with the droppings of an infected sheep. In moist situations, such as a waterlogged part of a field, the eggs hatch to set free a small larva called a miracidium, which is able to swim in a film of water on vegetation, and, of course, in pools of water. Unless it soon finds one of the fresh-water snails of the genus *Limnaea* it dies. Though these snails are common enough in really damp pasture land as well as in pools, the chance of a miracidium finding a snail before it dies is quite small. But as the parent fluke lays many eggs, the race continues to be reproduced.

Inside the snail the miracidium turns into a sporocyst larva. The sporocyst gives rise to a number of yet a third kind of larva called redia, and each redia forms a number of further redia. Each of these finally forms a number of the larvae called cercariae, and it was some like these which I discovered as a milky fluid. The cercariae on becoming free from the snail now form a cyst, and can, if encysted in water, live for as long as a year. If a cyst is made on aerial vegetation, however, it can survive only a few weeks.

No further development can take place unless the encysted larva is eaten by a sheep, when it makes its way to the liver and develops into a fluke. The whole cycle is shown in Fig. 6.

I have said that the original fluke parent must lay many eggs to give even one miracidium a chance to find, and bore into, a snail. Such a miracidium makes the most of its good fortune and from it many redia are produced. Each redia makes many cercariae. This immense production of cercariae is essential if even one is to be swallowed by a sheep. Of course, most farmers these days do not run their sheep on waterlogged ground if they can help it.

The same immense fertility is shown by the other flukes, and indeed by other internal parasites such as the tapeworms. When you obtain a snail which yields cercariae, just think of the prodigious waste of living units needed to carry on the parasitic species.

EARTHWORMS

During nights when it is damp and not too cold, earthworms of the species *Lumbricus terrestris* come above the surface of the soil throughout the year.   If sought with the aid of a torch-light, they can usually be found in fair numbers on suitable nights, both on bare garden soil and on lawns. Usually the tail of a worm will be inside the burrow, but the rest of the worm will be stretched along the surface of the soil, and the head-end may be searching actively for suitable food.   Such worms are sensitive to light and the vibrations of the earth.   The long worm apparently does not lie out on the top of the soil, at least during the early part of the night.   The other day I dug up a pair of long worms mating well below the soil level; the common earthworm mates on the surface.   The long worm makes big worm casts, the true earthworm (*L. terrestris*) making no cast.

Here are some experiments you can do with a worm.

Search for the worms with a diffuse light, e.g. a torch that is not too bright.

(1) *Does the worm respond to dim illumination?*

Allow the light from a torch held about 4 ft. from a worm to fall upon the worm for about 1 minute.   Usually the worm will make no special response, but will continue to lie still or to search for food.

(2) *Does the worm respond to a brighter illumination?*

Bring the torch closer to the worm, until it is about 6 in. from it, and hold the light steadily for a few seconds. Usually a worm will withdraw itself at once into its burrow, but with a dim light it may cease to move for a moment as if undecided what to do, withdrawing about $1\frac{1}{2}$ in., then pausing for a few seconds before snatching itself down its burrow.

(3) *Which part of the worm is sensitive to light?*

This may be investigated with the help of a convex lens. One about 1 in. across will serve, but a reading glass fitted with a handle is the most suitable. Using a dim light, locate a worm lying quietly on the soil, and get close to it. Then with the lens focus a spot of light onto its body near the mid region. If after a few seconds there is no response, move the spot of light forward along the body. As the spot approaches the head of the worm, the worm will suddenly snatch itself back into its burrow. This response is quite different from the slower and hesitating response given to general bright illumination. If you do not use a supplementary lens you may be able to manage with a torch fitted with a cardboard diaphragm having a small hole in the centre, but with this you may have to get very close to the worm.

(4) *Earth Vibration*

Find a worm partly lying across the soil surface, and stamp gently on the ground about 2 ft. from the worm. Normally the worm will snatch itself back into its burrow. If it does not, a firmer stamp will elicit the response.

(5) *Burrows*

The top $\frac{1}{4}$ in. or so of a burrow is usually lined with very fine black soil or rotting plant material (humus). This may easily be verified by digging out the surface soil containing the end of a burrow and splitting open this soil to expose the burrow. It will be apparent, also, that the burrows themselves have smooth linings made from a plaster of fine soil particles glued together. Frequently, leaves either

PLATE I

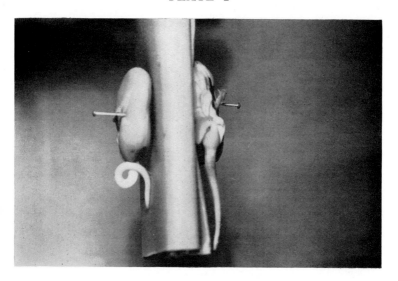

A—Two broad-bean seedlings which have been germinated in water in a 2-lb. jam-pot. The root of the left seedling curled round in a circle before continuing to grow downwards. The other seedling root grew downwards continuously.

B—Garden snail (*Cepaea hortensis*). Note the eye at the end of each long tentacle.

C—Two epiphragms from a single snail which had passed the winter just beneath the soil. There is a white spot on each epiphragm, near the top.

PLATE II

A—A bullyhead fish. These fish are usually found hiding under stones.

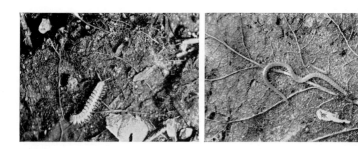

B—The millipede, *Polydesmus*. Note that on many segments it is quite easy to see that there are two legs on each side.

C—A centipede, *Geophilus*. These animals have only one leg on each side of a segment.

singly or in bunches, are pulled part way into the burrow, so that the outer portion sticks up vertically in the air. Even holly leaves are pulled down in this manner. Take some of these leaves and examine the part from below ground. Does its state now suggest that enzymes have been liberated onto it by the worm ?

(6) *Can the earthworm regenerate?*

Many animals have the power of regeneration developed to a remarkable extent. Such animals as the starfish can grow new arms if the old are lost, and the power of crayfish, lobsters and crabs to grow new limbs is well known. It is a widely held belief by countrymen that when an earthworm is cut into two parts each part will regenerate the necessary portion, i.e. the head end will grow a new tail and the tail a new head.

This assertion is easy enough to test. Obtain four large tins, such as large Oxo tins, usually obtainable from grocers, or even better, 7-lb. jam-tins from a confectioner. Pierce a few *small* holes in the lids and in the base, and half fill the tins with moist soil, being careful to see that no visible worms are included. Then at night catch forty worms (*Lumbricus terrestris*). It may take several nights if you have not a big lawn, but the worms can be stored in a tin of damp soil for several days. If you have some vacant garden you can also catch earthworms by digging for them with a fork—a spade may cut some of the worms into two. You will probably dig up some longworms as well, but if you compare all the worms you dig with one caught on the lawn, you will have no difficulty in recognising the differences between longworms and earthworms proper. You may like to make a list of the differences you can see.

Pinch through ten worms about one quarter of the way along the body—i.e. a little way in front of the saddle

c

(*clitellum*). Put all the heads and tails in one tin, replace the lid and sink the tin in the garden so that the lid comes about level with the surface of the soil. Repeat this for a second group of ten worms, but this time break each worm about half-way along, and so behind the clitellum. For a third experimental group break another ten worms about three-quarters of the way along the body from the head. Finally, put ten whole worms in the fourth tin, and sink the tin similarly to the others. These are control worms, and if they soon die, the experiment is no good. Death might occur because the worms are stretched rather tightly when caught by the light method on a lawn—or ten worms may not be able to live together for long in your tins. If these control worms live, however, it will show that the other worms could have lived, and if these others die it will be due to their being broken.

It is possible to place the tins in a cool place, instead of sinking them in the soil; but the latter method is more scientific, because the worms in sunken tins are in an environment very like their natural one, and regeneration is given every chance.

After a fortnight, and again after a month if it seems desirable, shake the contents of each tin separately onto a sheet of brown paper. First check the state of the controls, which should be quite lively. Then, from the other tins, find out whether the parts of worm are dead, or no different, or whether the wounds have healed and are beginning to regenerate segments of worm. Remember that living processes are slowed in cold weather and accelerated in warm weather, so the experiment takes longer in the winter months than it does in summer.

It is worth pointing out that the number of worms chosen for each tin need not be ten. You could do the experiment with five in each tin, or three, or only one. But if you used only one, parts of worm might die from some sickness not connected with the experiment. The more worms you use the more reliable will be the results. If one worm out of two in a tin died, the mortality would be 50 per cent, one out of five would be 20 per cent, one out of ten would be 10 per cent and one out of a hundred would be only 1 per cent. Biological experiments such as this frequently require mathematical treatment to find out exactly what the results mean, for the element of chance frequently creeps in to blur the result. In this experiment, for instance, some of the worms might be less viable—perhaps due to disease—than others, and so fail to regenerate, whereas the others would regenerate. If only one worm were used in each tin, quite fallacious conclusions might be drawn. The use of a large number of worms means that the chance of this kind of error is greatly lessened.

(7) *Can the tail of a worm burrow?*

Worms can move backwards quite easily. Is the tail end of an earthworm able to burrow in the soil?

Catch several large specimens of *L. terrestris* and pinch each into two parts in the region behind the clitellum. Place all the parts, which will consist of equal numbers of head and tail ends, on moist soil contained in a deep seed-box or a large tin. Leave the soil in a shady place, and if necessary protect it from birds with a sheet of glass. Return to it at the end of two hours or, if the experiment was set up in the evening, the next morning. It will be found that the tail portions are lying on the surface of the soil, although they will be quite lively. All the head ends have buried themselves. Make another inspection after two or three days.

I shall tell you here of a very curious incident which I witnessed on my lawn when I was living in Coventry. It was one of those misty September mornings when the grass is wet, but when the sun soon bursts through it is quite warm. About midday I was walking on the lawn, when I saw a loop of earthworm sticking up from the surface. I bent down to examine it more closely, and to my surprise the head of the worm had gone down the same burrow in which its tail was. Head and tail had apparently become jammed and the worm could neither penetrate its burrow nor emerge on the lawn. The loop of worm in the air was quite dried out, and presumably dead; but when I pulled the worm out, both the head end and the tail end were quite lively. I may add that we had few blackbirds or thrushes in the neighbourhood.

(8) *To trace an earthworm's burrow*

It is often claimed that an earthworm's burrow does not branch, and that it ends in a spherical nesting chamber lined with small stones.

An earthworm's burrow can be traced through the soil, but the feat is no easy one, especially in loose soils. Choose a burrow in firm soil, and with a spade dig a trench about 3 ft. long and 1 ft. wide, so that the mouth of the burrow is situated some 2 in. from the middle of one of the long sides of the trench. The trench, in the first instance, must be about 15 in. deep. With a thin steel table-knife pare away the side of the trench against the burrow, until the top 2 or 3 in. of the lumen of the burrow are exposed. The earth so pared away will usually fall into the trench and can conveniently be removed by hand or with a trowel. Continue to expose more of the burrow by slicing away more soil. Normally the walls of the burrow do not collapse, and are easy to see because the burrow is lined with fine soil particles cemented together. To reach the end of the burrow it may be necessary to enlarge or deepen the trench.

It is usually not advisable to start with a trench smaller than the dimensions given.   If one does start with a small hole, almost inevitably the initial hole has to be enlarged later, when it is much more difficult and when there is a danger of losing the worm's burrow through loose soil tumbling into it.

SNAILS

(1) *Homing experiment on snails*

On seashore rocks, exposed by the tide during low water, limpets are frequently to be seen clinging tightly to the surface.   Usually it is not possible to dislodge them with the hands, but if a limpet is given a *sudden* kick with the back of one's heel it may sometimes be dislodged.   Usually it will be found that there is a shallow depression on the rock which fits quite accurately the outline of the limpet's shell.   As limpets can be seen to move about when the rocks they inhabit are covered by the tide, the above observation suggests that each limpet returns to the same spot each time the tide recedes, and that either the limpet has worn a depression in the rock to fit its shell, or as the shell has grown, it has accommodated itself to a pre-existing depression.   In fact, observation has shown that limpets do have a well-marked ' homing instinct ', and in general return to the same place and take up the *same position*, time after time.   The advantage of this to the limpet is obvious—if its shell fits closely to the rock surface it will be capable of clinging tightly, and will lose very little water from under the edges of the shell during the hours of exposure.   During the spring tides (when the sea goes a long way out) you can check this by scraping conspicuous marks on several limpets' shells, and making a note of their positions when the tide is out.

Do ordinary garden snails (Helix aspersa) show a similar homing instinct?

In gardens where they are abundant, search during the daytime will reveal clusters of snails in holes in rockeries, under loose stones and in clumps of certain kinds of plants (e.g. irises). Disturbing such an aggregation of snails as little as possible, mark several of them in a distinctive manner with white paint. In the very late evening visit the clump to see whether the snails have dispersed (wet weather is most suitable); if they have, the next morning look again to see whether the marked snails have returned to the same place. The late evening visit is, of course, necessary to make sure that the snails have moved away. A stone in the garden painted at night would be in the same position the following morning, but there is no question of the stone having a homing instinct.

(2) *How many epiphragms does a garden snail make?*

If you can obtain a hibernating *Helix aspersa*, or one of brown and yellow *Cepaeas*, get it to come out of its shell by placing it in warm water. It takes no longer than ten minutes, and the epiphragm will be cast off very easily from the mouth of the shell. Do you ever get two or even three or more epiphragms (Plate I, c)?

(3) *Which external conditions influence the formation of epiphragms in snails?*

I know that snails kept in warm, dry conditions in the dark will soon produce an epiphragm, for many times I have had snails in jam-pots or honey-jars (with air holes in the top, or with pieces of cloth tied across the opening) and they have invariably produced epiphragms in a few days. I have sometimes wondered whether, in different environmental conditions, the snails would make epiphragms more quickly, or more slowly, or not at all. Here is an experiment to find the answers to these questions. I have not yet done it myself, but I shall do so next year.

I shall investigate the effects of cold, wet and light. First I shall gather thirty or forty garden snails (*Helix aspersa*) from under rockery stones and at the base of iris clusters, or else the yellow and brown banded snails (*Cepaea nemoralis*) which live in colonies along the hedgerow bottoms. In the summer these latter are most easily found after rain, especially in the evening, when they come out of their hiding places to feed.

The snails will be divided into four equal lots and each lot placed in a jam-jar. One jar will have a pad of wet cotton wool on its floor. Then a piece of cloth will be tied over each jar.

As in all such experiments which involve several factors, a control set will be needed for purposes of comparison, so I shall take one lot of snails in a dry jar and place it in a dark cupboard. I have found such snails make epiphragms readily in the summer when the air is relatively warm, and it is fair to say that they had the factor of warmth. Because of this I shall do the experiment in the summer. The control set of snails will therefore have in their environment the factors with which I am concerned, that is, there will be dryness, darkness and warmth (about 60–70° F.).

I shall then take from each of the other jars one of the factors. Dryness I shall remove with the pad of wet cotton wool (re-wetted as required). This jar will be placed in the dark, warm cupboard. From another I shall remove warmth by putting it in a refrigerator (not in the freezing part), where it will be dry and dark but not warm. Finally, with the third jar I shall remove darkness—that is, give it light by placing the jar outside the dark cupboard; and I shall leave the light on each night until the end of the experiment. So I shall have the control jar, and three experimental jars each lacking one of the factors present in the control jar, thus:

Jar	Factors present	Factors absent
Control	Darkness, dryness and warmth	None
Experimental 1.	Darkness and warmth	Dryness
Experimental 2.	Darkness and dryness	Warmth
Experimental 3.	Dryness and warmth	Darkness

It is easy enough to see through the glass wall of a jam-jar whether or not a snail has made an epiphragm, even though it is only quite a thin one. So each day I shall examine the jars and see if there is any difference between the time the control snails take to make epiphragms, and the time the experimental snails take. From these results it should be easy to assess the importance of the various factors. For example, in jar 3 with ' no darkness ' the snails may still be active some time after the control, and we can say that light inhibits the formation of epiphragms. On the other hand, light may make no difference, in which case these snails will produce epiphragms about the same time as the control snails. Of course, darkness at night is a normal factor of snail life.

(4) *The utilisation of dissolved oxygen by pulmonate water snails*

British fresh-water snails may be divided into two groups, the pulmonates and the operculates. The operculate snails breathe only dissolved oxygen, but the pulmonates are able to breathe oxygen from the air, because they have the lower part of the mantle cavity (Fig. 7) richly invested with blood vessels, so that the chamber functions as a lung (e.g. the great pond snail, *Limnaea stagnalis*).

Place a large pulmonate snail in a jam-pot full of pond

(or tap water) and observe it. From time to time the snail will ascend to the surface and apply its right-hand side to the surface of the water. The breathing aperture which leads into the lung will then be clearly visible as it is placed in contact with the air.

Pulmonate snails do, however, breathe some dissolved oxygen. This may be demonstrated as follows:

Take a full kettle of water and boil it for some minutes to

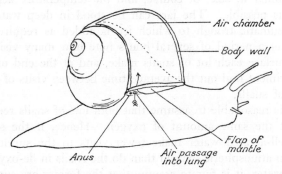

Fig. 7.—Simple diagram to show the position of the snail's lung.

expel all the dissolved gases. The water should now be poured into two or three bottles (remember to heat them or they will crack), corked, and then cooled down. A refrigerator is best because the temperature must be low —say, not above 5° C.; but in winter one could place the bottles of water outside for the night.

Now you require some clean glass containers—jam-jars will do but taller gas-jars are probably better. Fill one jar with well-aerated water. The aeration can be helped if the water is poured a number of times, with plenty of splashing, from one vessel to another. The jar of aerated water should be put with the corked bottles of unaerated water, so that all will reach the same low temperature. A few equal-sized pulmonates, e.g. the great pond snail, should be placed in water in another jar, and allowed to reach the same temperature. When everything has become quite cold, the experiment is performed as follows:

The cold unaerated water is poured slowly into a jar, whilst the other is once more poured a number of times, with plenty of splashing, from one jar to another.

Then place several snails in each jar. The snails should be similar in size, of course, and the temperature kept as low as possible. The jars can be stood in deep water in a pneumatic trough to which ice is added as required.

Over a period of several hours note how many visits to the surface each lot of snails make, and at the end of the experiment find out the average time between visits of both lots of snails.

It is reasonable to assume that both lots of snails require about the same amount of oxygen. Hence, if the snails in well-aerated water make fewer visits to the surface to obtain atmospheric oxygen than do the snails in de-oxygenated water, it is fair to assume that the former are supplementing the oxygen they obtain from the air by absorbing some of the oxygen dissolved in the water. (Oxygen will dissolve in the boiled water, but it takes some hours to do so.)

Operculate snails may be identified by the presence of a small plate, or operculum, on the tail. This operculum is used to close the mouth of the shell when the snail withdraws inside. Operculate snails, being unable to utilise atmospheric oxygen, are usually found mainly in well-aerated water, such as rivers and streams, and windswept lakes. They are sometimes to be found in canals, especially where the water is well-aerated for some reason. In a stretch of the Shropshire Union Canal the writer found colonies of the operculate snail on the stonework where the tow-path went under the bridges. Here the canal was fairly exposed and wind action caused an almost perpetual ' chopping ' of the water against the stone, and this must have aided oxygenation of the water. Lakes usually have one or more sides where the water, due to the prevailing wind, is more usually thrown into ripples. It would be worthwhile, in suitable lakes, comparing the snail population from the ' ripple ' side with that from the ' smooth ' side. Where streams or drainage effluents trickle into ponds or lakes, they sometimes have the effect of raising the concentration of dissolved oxygen in the immediate locality.

Before I leave the gastropods I should like to mention two species for which you may care to look. The first is the blind snail (*Caeciliodes acicula*) and is so called because, unlike other snails, it has no black pigment in its eyes. It is quite tiny, its shell being about 5 mm. long (Fig. 8). It is whitish in colour, and I had never seen a specimen until one day three years ago. I was sitting on the lawn by the rose garden idly dreaming, when suddenly my eyes picked out an empty shell among the surface

FIG. 8.—The shell of a blind snail.

granules of soil. It was so tiny that I could not believe it was an adult, but reference to *British Snails* by Ellis[1] left me in no doubt. I have since searched several times for this snail, but have not been able to find one. It lives underground, so that your best chance of finding it is when digging the garden.

The second gastropod, for which I had been on the lookout during the last twenty years or so, came to me in this way. An old friend called on me one day with a jar

[1] *British Snails*, H. E. Ellis, Oxford.

containing several white slugs. He said, ' I'll bet you've never come across slugs with shells on their tails '.

I replied, ' No, I have not, but I have spent many years searching for them. Their name is *Testacella*. They live underground, and are carnivorous'.

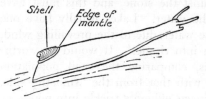

FIG. 9.—The slug *Testacella*.

My friend then said, ' Well, here are some for you which I caught when we were digging the rose garden at Derby Farm Institute'. There before my eyes were a number of these slugs (Fig. 9). I have always looked for *Testacella* when digging the gardens of several widely-separated houses in which I have lived, but I have never come across one myself. You may have better luck.

MILLIPEDES AND CENTIPEDES

Movement in millipedes and centipedes

Under bark and stones, in manure heaps and piles of garden refuse, as well as in the detritus on the floor of a wood, you will come across millipedes and centipedes. These animals have elongated bodies, sometimes extremely elongated. The bodies have a number of segments each of which bears legs. In the millipedes the segments bear two pairs of legs, whilst in the centipedes a single pair of legs is carried on each segment. A further difference between the two groups is that millipedes have short antennae, whilst those of the centipedes are long—almost half the body length. There is really no difficulty in distinguishing between members of the two groups (Plate II, B and C).

A common millipede is *Iulus terrestris*, which has a slaty

black colour and is more or less cylindrical. It is composed
of up to seventy segments and can curl into a tight spiral.
When it moves it does so slowly, and if you watch it cross
a piece of paper you will no doubt be delighted to discover
the apparent waves which run down each set of legs, wave
following wave in an orderly way. The legs are said to
move in *metachronal* rhythm. *Iulus* shows this metachronal rhythm better than any of the other millipedes or
centipedes, but the long pale golden yellow centipede,

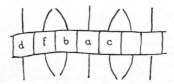

FIG. 10.—A diagram to illustrate how the legs of the centipede,
Geophilus, move the body. Suppose this to be a portion of the
centipede's body moving from left to right. The legs shown as
(*a*) would be moving, unconnected to the ground, until they
reached a position similar to the legs of (*c*). Then their tips
would contact the ground and the body would be pulled forwards.
The legs would straighten (*a*) and then point backwards (*b*) to
the end of their stroke. The legs on (*f*) have just arrived at the
front of their unattached forward stroke.

Geophilus, shows, under a hand lens, the individual leg
movement better than *Iulus*. Careful examination will
reveal that the pair of legs on a segment act like the two
oars of a man rowing a boat (Fig. 10); they reach forward
together and then swing backwards together. The power
stroke of both boat and centipede is the same: it is the
backstroke where either the blade of the oar or the tip of
the leg *appear* to move towards the hind end. However,
the oar blade is immersed in water and the centipede's leg-
tip is fixed to the ground: it is the boat's and the centipede's

bodies which move forward. The 'recovery' strokes of boat and centipede are also the same. The oar blades are lifted from the water and swung towards the front of the boat, whilst the centipede's legs are lifted from the ground and swung forward towards the head. The power strokes now start again.

How can you verify my statement? Well, obtain a *Geophilus* centipede and place it on a sheet of white paper. It does not move rapidly and can easily be controlled.

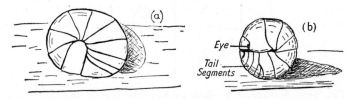

FIG. 11.—(*a*) *Glomeris* (a millipede); (*b*) *Armadillum vulgaris* (a wood louse). Both are rolled up, ×2½.

Bring it close to a good light and watch the tip of one leg, *and the shadow of it.* You will need a hand lens, of course, and it may take you a few seconds to teach yourself to concentrate on a single leg, but it is well worth the effort. Are the leg-tip and the shadow in contact on the back swing? Are they on the forward swing? Does the leg-tip move on the back swing?

While on the subject of millipedes and centipedes I would like to mention a millipede called *Glomeris*, a curious animal which at first sight suggests a tiny black armadillo. It has a very convex back, and consists of several segments, fewer than is usual in millipedes. When you catch one it will roll itself into a ball, so that it looks very like the pill woodlouse (*Armadillum vulgaris*) when that is rolled into a ball. However, the plate arrangement of the two creatures is quite different, and the *Glomeris* is far from being a perfect sphere (Fig. 11a). What happens if you place it on its back on a smooth surface ?

SPIDERS

(1) *Spiders' webs*

The web-building spiders recognise the presence of prey in their webs by the vibrations caused by its struggles. Often web-building spiders do not remain in the web. Instead they hide somewhere near at hand, but maintain physical contact with the web, often by means of a taut signal line. One end of the signal line is attached to the web, while the other is fixed to a convenient object by the spider's hiding place. One foot of the spider rests on this end of the line. When a fly becomes entangled in the web vibrations are transmitted along the signal thread and are perceived by the lurking spider, which normally rushes to the web and kills the prey by biting it with its poison fangs.

The hiding place of the concealed spider may often be discovered if one can find the ' signal line ' and trace it from the web to its point of origin.

Alternatively, if a grass stalk is twiddled in the web to make it vibrate in the same manner as when a fly is ensnared, the spider may frequently be caused to rush into the web. Usually the spider discovers the deception before it actually reaches the grass stalk, and retires hurriedly.

Not only the spiders that make the beautiful geometrical 'orb webs', but also those that make a web around the mouth of a tunnel in the earth may be deceived in this way.

(2) *Nature of spider's web*

Orb-web-making spiders coat certain of the silken strands with a sticky fluid. Such coated threads are ' twanged ' by the spider, with the result that the sticky fluid is thrown into separate droplets arranged along the length of the thread as tiny liquid beads. The droplets of liquid are quite visible under a hand lens.

Obtain a portion of the web of a garden spider by pressing a piece of clean glass onto the web. The web will stick to the glass and may be then conveniently examined.

Which threads are sticky, the spokes or the spiral ?

Is the very centre of the web sticky ?

Does the web of the cobweb spider have a sticky fluid ?

Why does the spider not stick to its own web ? You may have to look up the answer in a book (e.g. *A Book of Spiders* by W. S. Bristowe).

The webs of certain spiders are to be found throughout the winter, and are occasionally made into conspicuous festoons by hoar frost. On the 6th February, 1949, I found a spider frozen into its web on the front of a beehive. (Foolishly I did not try to thaw the spider with cold water and see if it were still alive, so I missed a simple but instructive experiment.)[1]

What types of insects do such spiders catch at this season of the year ? Try to find out by examining the webs for remains, and note which kinds of insects fly on the warmer days during winter. Occasionally, nebulae of 'winter gnats' will be seen dancing in the afternoon sun, and on very warm days hive bees will take short flights. Hive bees, of course, are not caught in spiders' webs. If they

[1] It is best to use cold water to thaw a spider, allowing it to become warm gradually. Living material (protoplasm) if rapidly frozen, freezes without suffering much damage from ice crystals forming, because the crystals are very small and do not rupture the cell boundaries. However, if frozen protoplasm is thawed quickly by means of high temperature, large ice crystals are first formed and they do the damage which would have been done by slow freezing.

PLATE III

A—Water crickets skating on the surface of a porridge plate full of water. They had been caught skating along the water of a stream, in January.

B—Winter aphid eggs on an apple-tree branch. The eggs are really black, but shine brilliantly in sunlight.

C—A female flower of yew, showing the globule of mucilage which traps male pollen grains. Pollination is at the end of February and beginning of March.

PLATE IV

A   B

A—A young common sow-thistle plant, showing a serpentine mine.

B—A chrysalis of an orange-tip butterfly. It had fed on the jack-by-the-hedge plant before pupating. The plant tissues are now dead and fungi are growing on them. The orange-tip caterpillars usually leave this food plant before pupating.

C—A leaf miner living in a holly leaf, just below the upper epidermis, which latter has been stripped off to show the fly pupa and the careful way its droppings lie as far away as possible from its eating places.

do become entangled they are strong enough to burst their way out.

(3) *How long does the garden spider keep a web?*

The authority on spiders mentioned above (W. S. Bristowe), speaking of the garden spider, says:

> 'Daily in summer these superb craftswomen destroy their old webs, except for the frame, and then build a new one in the space of about half an hour.' [1]

You can easily test this assertion by placing tiny pieces of tissue-paper (or shaking face-powder) on the sticky spiral strands of a web. Do this first thing in the morning and see if your recognition substances are still there at nightfall. If they have disappeared the web must have been renewed during the day. If the pieces of tissue are still there, look again in the morning. If they have now disappeared the web must have been renewed during the night. Should your little experiment show the web to be renewed during the day, then arrange frequent visits to find out the approximate time. If the web turns out to be remade at night, visit it with a torch. You will no doubt find a lot of spiders in their webs after dark, though they are concealed during the day-time. Of course, if you are a keen naturalist, you will wish to see the spider actually making her web.

Phosphorescence—how to make sure of seeing it

One dark night in Shropshire, when I was a boy, I saw in a hedgerow a curious pale white light—quite steady in its glow and perfectly still. Very curious, I bent over it and saw what appeared to be a black beetle larva shining at its tail end. With considerable excitement I trapped the insect in a matchbox, and hurried on to the village institute to

[1] W. S. Bristowe, *Spiders*, King Penguin, p. 22.

D

which I was going. Inside, I called to some of my friends to see my phosphorescent creature. They clustered round and I opened my matchbox. To my dismay there was just a blackish insect, not like ordinary insects but more like a beetle larva, and I was laughed at by my fellows. I put the box disconsolately in my pocket.

When I reached home later in the night I opened the box again in my darkened bedroom, and lo! there it glowed again, coldly and steadily. For several minutes the light persisted, and then it was shut off once more.

I took it to school the next day. The biology master was distinctly pleased. He said it was an adult female glow-worm, a beetle where the male had normal wings but the female was without wings. Her last three abdominal segments could produce the entrancing light which so appealed to me. The glow-worms must have been quite rare in our area, for no one else had seen one. How can a single female (remember that it was *wingless*), turn up like that? I do not know. Later on I came across hedge-banks which showed a myriad phosphorescent lights, and the glow-worms were everywhere. It is a sight well worth seeing.

Very occasionally since then I have seen a phosphorescent streak along the road near timber-felling operations. This is due to a fungus occasionally present in logs. To make sure of seeing phosphorescent light, obtain a piece of fresh herring and place it on an open plate. Leave it for one or two days, and then examine it in the dark. If it is not glowing leave it a little longer. This phosphorescence is caused by bacteria, but I believe that in glow-worms it comes from certain tissues.

Luminescence from inorganic chemicals is not rare, especially from the sulphides (e.g. barium suphide used in luminous watches), and luminescence from living things is better called bio-luminescence. The chemicals concerned with this are called luciferin and luciferase, the latter being a catalyst (or enzyme) which, in the presence of water, oxydises the luciferin to oxyluciferin, which is the luminous substance. Oxyluciferin can be reduced again to luciferin. The glow-worms can shut off their lights by preventing oxygen reaching the active tissue.

There is an interesting case of false phosphorescence which you may come across in a moss called *Schistostega pennata* (there is no common name). This moss is very local—that is, it does not grow in many places; but where it does grow, it is sometimes very abundant. In his book on Mosses and Liverworts, E. V. Watson says:

'The peculiar light-reflecting power of the protonema, which as Dixon states, " gives a beautiful golden-green lustre to the plant and seems to fill with light the crevices and caves where it grows ", is due to its remarkable cell structure. Instead of the weft of branching threads that forms the protonema in most mosses, *Schistostega* develops a plate of almost lens-shaped cells. The convex outer walls enable these cells to act as light traps, the green sheen that is produced depending on this fact and on the position of the chloroplasts which are clustered against the " back " wall of each cell.'[1]

The protonema of mosses referred to grows from moss spores, and forms the structure from which the plants usually called mosses grow. Discussing the kind of places (habitats) which *Schistostega* seems to prefer for growth, Watson goes on,

'Its most characteristic habitats are sandstone caves, rabbit holes and deep fissures amongst sandstone rocks—always

[1] E. V. Watson, *British Mosses and Liverworts*, pp. 203-4, Cambridge University Press.

where the light intensity is very low. It also grows on granite and other siliceous rocks. In west Cornwall it is extremely abundant in old mine shafts.'

If you find some of this moss, have a look at it in the dark. Ought it to continue glowing ?

CHAPTER THREE

INSECTS

HIBERNATION

I HAVE put the insects in a section by themselves because there are so many of them, and the naturalist is continually coming across them. Although they are more numerous in the warmer months of the year some can be found at every season, and it is a continual pleasure to meet with insects in the late autumn, winter, and early spring.

I have, too, had a number of surprises from insects. I shall relate only two. One night in the middle of October, I was photographing a flower of the succulent plant called *Stapelia*—not an English plant, but one easily grown in a warm, light window or in a greenhouse. The flowers are star-shaped, the five petals being of a greeny cream colour thickly covered with blotches of very dark maroon. It gives off a powerful smell, which could easily be mistaken for the stench of rotting meat. In fact, these flowers are pollinated by blowflies, which presumably mistake them for pieces of meat.

I took the photograph in my room after dark. The room was quite warm, but I had seen no flies in it for several days. Just as I was about to press the shutter trigger on my camera, a blowfly came buzzing about the lamp I was using to illuminate the flower. The lamp was situated about 6 in. from the flower—to which the fly now transferred itself, and began to probe about. I clicked my camera joyfully and obtained two pictures. I had no reason to expect a blowfly in my room, and I had not seen one previously about my light when taking photographs. Was it the foul smell of the *Stapelia* flower that attracted it ? And where had the fly come from ? Presumably it was beginning to hibernate in some cranny it had found behind the furniture or skirting board, but the warmth, and the stench of the *Stapelia*, had enticed it out.

My other example also concerns hibernation. I was painting the inside of an upstairs window a few days before the *Stapelia* incident, and had to open the catch in order to push the windows up and down so that I could paint the horizontal surfaces. The catch was of the type which is attached to the upper frame, and has a lock bar which swings over the joint between the upper and lower windows, securing them by entering a clip on the lower window frame. I left the windows open for two days with the lock bar pushed back against the plate on the top window. When I came to close the windows and secure them by means of the lock bar, imagine my surprise to find that a queen wasp had crawled between the lock bar and metal plate which houses it. She was quite quiet and had evidently chosen this site as a suitable place in which to hibernate.

I have always been on the alert to find hibernating insects during the winter months, and have also welcomed the appearance of flying insects. Once, during the first week of February in a very cold winter, I was walking across Derbyshire moorland and came upon a small stream that hurried down to the valley, but which here and there had small pools. On some of these were small groups (five or six individuals) of the pond skater, *Velia* (Plate III, A). These live on the dead bodies of insects carried down by the stream, and can dart rapidly about to make contact with them. I found that the *Velias* could live some months without food, and you might like to tackle the problem of how long they can survive. I kept mine in a jam-jar with some water weed in it, and it could be argued that the *Velias* were using the pond weed or small aquatic creatures as food. This could be tested quite easily by setting up a control jar which contained only filtered stream water and *Velias*.

Insects, of course, can pass the winter as eggs (e.g. greenfly); or as larvae (e.g. caterpillar of the large yellow underwing moth, *Triphaena pronuba*); or as pupae (e.g. cabbage white butterfly); or in the adult form. You will probably know several examples of the last. Two-spot ladybirds seem to gather together in fairly large numbers—fifty or more is usual—to pass the winter under loose bark or in old brickwork. Sometimes builders come across these ' hibernation aggregations ', and occasionally there are so many ladybirds that the men are amazed and a note appears in the local paper. Other insects form similar aggregations to pass the winter, and a favoured place is under the loose bark of fallen logs. In the Coventry nature reserve I found under bark a ' hibernation aggregation ' of about 20 ichneumon wasps of the species *Ichneumon extensorius*. When an insect passes the winter in the adult form it would seem sufficient if only mated females did so, for there would then be no need for the males in spring. Most insects, of course, merely lay their eggs and leave them to hatch, the larvae having to fend for themselves. There are a few species where the mother does look after the young ones (e.g. the earwig), and of course in the social insects (ants, bees and wasps) the larvae are tended by females. Males play no part in rearing larvae. We can, then, ask the following question:

Are insects that pass the winter as adults always female?

It does not require an experiment to answer this question, for it can be answered by direct observation. You must catch a number (the more the better) of the early specimens of each species you wish to investigate, but you will have to be able to distinguish the males from the females. This is sometimes easy, but sometimes difficult. Types in which the sexes are easily recognised include the brimstone butterfly, *Gonepteryx rhamni*, which is often flying in March. The females are a pale greenish yellow, easily mistaken when on the wing for a large cabbage white, whilst the males are a sulphur-yellow. The early bumble bees, too, are worth investigating. If they are females they will have pollen baskets on their hind legs, and their antennae will have twelve segments. Males have no pollen baskets, and their antennae have thirteen segments. In addition, the males have a pronounced tuft of 'hairs' on the face.

A third group easy to examine is the mosquitoes, which in some houses can be caught on the walls of warm rooms in spring. Male mosquitoes have very bushy (feathery) antennae, whilst the antennae of females are slender threads carrying only a few hairs.

Earwigs pass the winter as adults, and may often be found in the hollow stems of plants such as hogwood. The males have much stouter forceps at the end of the body than do the females, and I suggest you make earwigs a fourth group.

It is not justifiable to assume that the results for one species will be the same as those for another. In other words, each species must be investigated independently. If you do investigate these four species you will see the truth of this statement.

BLOWFLIES

Some corpses are buried by beetles. Others are not and will remain lying on the surface of the ground. Usually these become 'fly-blown' and in a few days become populated with the maggots of blowflies.

Is there more than one kind of blowfly which deposits its eggs on the corpses of animals?

The experiment should be carried out sometime during hot weather. First obtain some suitable meat, the corpse of a rat, or bird, or if these are not obtainable, sixpennyworth of cat's meat from the butchers'. This will very likely be a hunk of lights, and when you receive it, it will be very obvious why it has the name ' lights'. Actually, of course, lights are lungs, and really contain very little meat. Some of the cartilaginous tubes called bronchi will very likely be visible. Place the meat in the garden, preferably in a sunny spot, and if necessary protect it from dogs and cats with wire netting. Alternatively, cut off portions of the lights and hang them up in jam-jars in suitable places.

Very soon blowflies will appear. At first only the large ' blue-bottles ' (*Calliphora*) will visit the bait, but many eggs will be laid, though these are usually more or less under the meat, or in holes (e.g. bronchial tubes). In hot weather the eggs will hatch within a day and the maggots begin to feed under and in the meat, which now begins to exude the powerful stench characteristic of meat ' going off '. You will find then that other flies come to visit the meat, and after the second or third day it is often covered by the much smaller ' green-bottles ' (*Lucilia*), and no large blue-bottles may be present.

You may have observed several other different kinds of flies walking about on the meat, but this is not proof that they have laid eggs upon it. To test that you will have to rear the adults from the maggots you obtain in the meat.

If your meat has been kept in a jam-jar you will find that there are always too many maggots present, and the edible parts of the lights are soon consumed. There is a most powerful stench, and a dark grey ooze forms in which the maggots wallow for a time; but soon the maggots try to escape, presumably to find fresh food. You must put small numbers of maggots (say nine or ten) in different jam-jars and put $1\frac{1}{2}$ in. of garden soil in the bottom. Place more meat with the maggots and put on stiff cloth covers. If the cloth is at all loose in its weave, the maggots often escape through what you had considered maggot-proof material. The maggots grow quickly in hot weather. After a few days the maggots are restless, and the dark line down their backs that marks their food canals disappears. They have stopped feeding and are ready to pupate.

You can do a little experiment here. Keep some jars as they are, but take an equal number of jars and clean them out, putting the maggots back with clean soil. Which maggots pupate first, those who have to live in the accumulation of their end-products, or those whose end-products have been removed ?

From the pupae, blowflies will soon emerge and you should be able to see whether all the blowflies are the same or whether there is more than one type.

An experiment on blowfly pupation

The pupation of the maggot and the emergence of the adult are both interesting events. It is easy to tell when a maggot is on the verge of pupation, for it becomes shorter and fatter, and its previously pointed head end becomes rounded. Then the whitish maggot skin turns first creamy and finally a polished light brown. At the same time the maggot skin becomes hard. The pupa of the fly is within the maggot skin, which is now called the puparium. Examine the puparium with a hand lens. How many segments can you count ? Can you see the spiracles which were present at the hind end of the maggot's last segment ? If you can, this will be a sure way of telling the head end of a puparium from the tail end.

As the pupa gradually develops, the puparium becomes darker in colour until it is blackish-brown. Then the fly bursts its way out of the puparium, leaving an empty case with a flap which the fly had pushed aside to escape. Which end is this flap? And how many segments are involved in it?

When a fly emerges it is creamy grey in colour, and has undeveloped wings. It also has a creamy white bladder, called the ptilinum, extruding from its head, and which it pulsates to help to pull itself upwards through the soil. You should have a number of dark puparia in a jam-jar (with lid) where you can see them easily and often. These will begin to hatch and you should inspect the jar at intervals until you see a newly-hatched fly. Take it out of the jar and examine its wings, which are small and crumpled. Also examine the ptilinum which projects from the fly's forehead. You should be able to see it pulsate—it swells and extends forward, and then is retracted for each pulsation. The wings are soon inflated, gradually the fly darkens in colour, its skin hardens, and the ptilinum is withdrawn into the forehead.

When the flies are hatching freely, it is very instructive to dissect away some of the wall of the puparium, and if you take due regard of the spiracles at the hind end you can remove the dorsal wall using a needle only. Fine forceps may be a help to some people. Look at the fly through a hand lens and you will be amazed at the compact way it is fitted into the puparium: also you will be certain to see the ptilinum pulsating.

An experiment on blowfly maggots

It is claimed that the stimulus which causes a blowfly maggot to pupate is a hormone produced by a gland in the head end, which diffuses fluid throughout the maggot's body and so affects every part. Is this claim justified?

You may easily test it as follows: Take two jam-pots and put soil from the garden into each.   Then take forty maggots about to pupate, and put twenty of them into one jar to act as a control.   Around the middle of each of the other twenty maggots tie a piece of cotton, drawing the knot so tight that it just fails to cut the maggot into halves.   If you miscalculate and do cut the maggot, replace it with a fresh one.   The taut cotton ring should prevent fluid from the head of the maggot passing into the hind end.   Tie all twenty maggots in the same way, and put them in the experimental pot.   When the control maggots have pupated, look at the experimental ones.   You should find them with the front end pupated and the hind ends still maggot.   Can you suggest an explanation if both ends have pupated, as sometimes occurs ?

Demonstration of negative phototaxis in blowfly larvae

' Taxes ' are forced movements of the whole of an animal in response to a directional stimulus such as the rays of light emitted from a small light source (ideally a point source).   If the animal persistently moves towards the stimulus, it is said to have a positive taxis, whereas if it moves away from the stimulus it is said to show a negative taxis.

Obtain some blowfly maggots, either by exposing a piece of meat to flies for a few days in summer, or bought from a fishing-tackle shop, where they are sold as ' gentles '.   Shake the maggots onto a table in a room with only one window. The maggots will at first crawl in all directions, but in a few seconds the vast majority will be crawling *away* from the light.

In a darkened room shake some maggots onto a large table (or the floor) and hold a flashlamp so that its beam shines along the table.   The maggots will soon nearly all be crawling away from the light along the direction of the beam. If the light is gradually moved round in a circular path the maggots will change their direction of crawling so that they continue to move directly away from the light. In this way they can be caused to turn through a complete circle.

If two lights of equal power are held at the same distance from the maggots, so that their beams shine at right angles

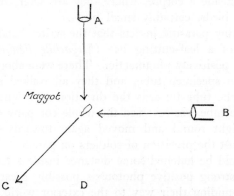

FIG. 12.—Blowfly maggot retreating from the lamps of equal power, A and B, along the line to C.

to one another, the maggots will crawl away at an angle of 45° to each beam (Fig. 12). By varying the power of the lights (or, what comes to the same thing, altering the distance from the maggots of one light while keeping the other fixed) it is easy to see that the maggots move along what we may call the 'resultant' of the two beams, i.e. that path which removes them most quickly from the effect of both lights.

Blue-bottle (*Calliphora erythrocephala*) maggots lose their negative response to light just before they are about to pupate. This is an advantageous adaptation because it enables the maggots to move away from the corpse on which they have been reared, and pupate at a distance of a yard or more. I suppose that we should expect them to travel only at night, safely from ichneumon wasps and birds, but that is not my experience.

Blowfly maggots, then, until ready to pupate show negative phototaxis, as when, for instance, the corpse on which they are feeding is disturbed by a fox or bird. This response to light has value for them in that it tends to keep the maggots inside a corpse, where they are safer from being eaten by birds, certainly small birds.

Some tiny parasitic insects that the writer hatched from the cell of a leaf-cutting bee (*Megachile ligniseca*) were markedly positively phototactic. There were about fifty of them in a specimen tube, and they all walked along the walls of the tube towards the direction of brightest light. When the tube was reversed the whole company of insects turned right round and moved again towards the light with almost the precision of soldiers on parade. Normally these would be hatched some distance inside a tree-trunk, and the strong positive phototaxis possibly greatly assists them in finding their way to the exterior world.

BALANCERS

There is some evidence that it is more difficult for a two-winged insect to fly than it is for a four-winged insect. The hind wings of *Diptera* (two-winged flies) are modified to form a pair of slender rods called halteres or balancers. Each balancer ends in a small knob and rather resembles a tiny pin projecting from the side of the thorax. It is probable that the halteres have the function of gyroscopes, because when the insects are in flight the halteres vibrate rapidly. This can easily be verified if a large fly is caught and held by one wing in such a way that the other wing is free to move. Under these conditions the free wing will perform flying movements, and if the haltere of that side is observed through a lens it will be seen to vibrate rapidly when the wing is in motion.

In this connection an observation made on the beetle *Sisypus* and reported in the periodical *Nature* is of interest. During flight this beetle places its front legs on the edges of the wing cases, so that the feet (tarsi) point upwards, and vibrate rapidly.

BEETLES

Disposal of corpses by sexton beetles

Although one may occasionally find the bodies of dead birds and, more rarely, of such small mammals as mice, moles and rats, the number of these corpses encountered is small when compared with the numbers of birds and mammals that must die through one cause or another.

There are several reasons for this scarcity of corpses. One reason is that during the summer months many such corpses are buried by

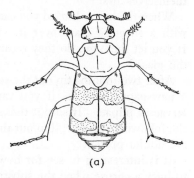

(a)

Fig. 13.—Sexton beetle (*Necrophorus investigator*) ×2.

sexton beetles. There are seven species of sexton beetles (genus *Necrophorus*), four of which are reasonably common, and usually when a dead animal is discovered one or more of these beetles will be found beneath it. The beetles all have the general shape shown in Fig. 13, and six of the species have two reddish-orange bands across the black wing cases (elytra).

Experiments with sexton beetles

Frequently, even in large towns, sexton beetles may be attracted by suitable bait (e.g. a fowl's head or a dead rat) left in the garden. The bait should be inaccessible to rats, and may conveniently be suspended in a 2-lb. jam-pot from a tree. If you can obtain sexton beetles on the bait in the jam-jar you will then be able to watch how the beetles proceed to bury the bait in loose soil. It will be an excellent thing if you can obtain a flower-pot, say one measuring 6 in. or so across the top, and fill it with garden soil to an inch below the rim. Then put your bait and beetles on it. Do the beetles start to bury the bait at once, or do they bury themselves first ?

When the bait is buried you can sink the pot in the ground with a sheet of glass over it. Do the sextons reappear ? If you let them go, do they return and try to enter through the glass ?

After two months tip out the soil from the flower-pot onto a newspaper, and see if you can find any signs of beetle larvae or pupae. If so put them back and leave them until the following spring. Tip out the soil again and see if there are adults present.

It is interesting to see for how long sextons will attempt to bury a corpse when the substratum is solid, such as four bricks laid together to form a rectangle, or a concrete or tarmac path. Place a layer of soil about $\frac{1}{4}$ in. thick on the substratum, and then put on the animal to be buried together with two or three sextons. Do they soon desist from their efforts to bury their booty ? You could also find out whether a single sexton will endeavour to bury a corpse by itself

Corpses of rats, rabbits and moles attract such carnivorous birds as crows and magpies. That means that beetles under the corpse are themselves in danger of being eaten. Do you think that the bands of yellowish-brown on the black elytra (wing covers) is a form of warning coloration, so that old birds do not attempt to eat them ? You might be able to test this by throwing a few dead sextons to a pen of hens, or even better to hens on free range. Why do I suggest that the free-range hens would be more desirable ?

Finally, I think you should examine the external structure of a sexton in order to discover how well it is adapted to burying corpses. The legs are all sturdy and have rather long spines to enable them to get a grip in the ground. The sexton is thick and strong looking in the body; the elytra are hard and offer a fairly flat surface so that an object on them will not easily slip off. The thorax too is rather flat, and has ridges that increase its holding power.

Any dead animal encountered should be turned over to see if there are sextons beneath it. Some of the sextons will be found to be covered with mites which run actively about the beetle's body and are quite difficult to dislodge. A puff of tobacco smoke is often successful in causing them to leave the beetle's body. They are parasites living at the expense of their beetle hosts. Formerly they were considered to be symbionts, living with the beetles as partners.

Sextons are usually the first beetles to visit a corpse, but if a corpse remains unburied other kinds of beetles follow in their turn. Many of these belong to the group *Clavicornia* (e.g. the beetle *Hister*). These beetles are called carrion beetles and do not attempt to bury the host. They are often very smooth, highly polished, black beetles, which when disturbed tuck their legs under their bodies and remain quite still. In this condition they are extremely difficult to pick up in the fingers, and possibly birds picking over a

E

carcass in which they are dwelling find it equally difficult to hold them, even if they see them. Many other kinds of insect lie quite still when molested—as do some spiders. I once saw a frog attacked and turned over by my dog, and it lay quite still on its back. I am positive that it made a quite separate movement to put its front feet over its ears. Why did it ?

Carnivorous water beetles

Try the effect of placing a carnivorous water beetle (e.g. the great diving beetle—*Dytiscus marginalis*) in a jam-jar which is about two-thirds full of pond water. After two days add a large horse leech or some comparable water creature (e.g. small fish), and watch what happens.

Others of the large pond beetles can be used for this observation, and so can the larvae of *Dytiscus*.

Click beetles

It is always interesting to obtain beetles alive, and to examine them through a hand lens. I am not suggesting that you must inevitably collect beetles as a group, but there are numerous beetles worth seeking. For instance, it is worth trying to obtain the species of the weevil that lays its eggs in green hazel nuts, one egg for each nut. The larva lives in its nut until the nut is ripe and falls to the ground. Then the larva bites a neat hole through the shell and descends into the soil to pupate. It is worth while to attempt to follow the emergence and pupation of the larvae in a jam-jar with 2 in. or so of soil on the bottom. Keep a good supply of the nuts in dry jam-jars so that you can observe emergence.

It is, however, the click beetles that I wish to discuss. There is a whole group of them, mostly from $\frac{1}{4}$ in. to $\frac{1}{2}$ in. in length. They are narrowish insects with a hard exoskeleton, which in the common ones is dark brown in colour. These creatures are the adults of the wireworms which eat the roots of various farm crops, especially grasses and cereals.

In summer the adults of wireworms are easily caught by sweeping an insect net through grass, or even with the hand alone. Having caught one, lay it on its back on your hand. The beetle will remain quiescent for a second or two, but will then arch itself upwards at the join behind the head and shortly, with a distinct ' click ', will flip into the air and descend the right way. Probably it will be lost to you in the grass.

In a clear room, or in a backyard, see how many jumps it can make before it is exhausted. How many would you expect ?

Look at the under-surface with a lens and examine the little peg which protrudes backwards from the first thoracic segment and is received by a groove in the second thoracic segment. It is this peg that makes the ' click '.

Dor beetles in dung (*Geotrupes*)

These beetles are about 1 in. long. They are black on top, some species dull, others shiny metallic. Underneath some species have a metallic blue sheen.

In April, pairs of male and female beetles appropriate patches of manure, both horse and drying cow dung being suitable. Burrowing beneath a patch of dung the beetles excavate a tunnel from which lead quite large (about 1 in. long) chambers. Both beetles assist in stocking the chambers with manure from the surface. The female beetle then lays one egg in each packet of dung, which, indeed, is a fairly large store of food. This takes place in April or May.

The existence of the beetle-burrow beneath the dung is easy to check, for there is a round hole about half an inch in diameter in the manure, surrounded often by a pile of soil. From this hole a tunnel delves into the soil, going down as much as a foot or even more. With a spade the

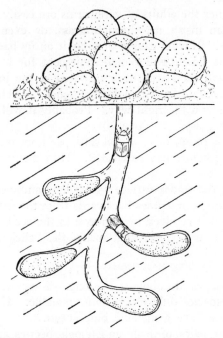

Fig. 14.—Diagram of the galleries made by dor beetles under horse manure. Both male and female beetles are present, and are completing the provision of manure in the side chambers. One egg will be laid on each batch of dung, near the central tunnel.

burrow can be excavated and the nurseries discovered. Very likely the dor beetle will be present and can be caught quite easily (Fig. 14). A boy to whom I had told this went later in the day into a grazing field by his house, and the following day he brought me twelve of these beetles.

The eggs hatch later on, the larvae eat their pile of dung, and pupate. The adult beetles emerge from the soil next spring.

I think that the beetles would be quite easy to rear. In the spring of 1958 I dug under cow dung which had the characteristic round hole, and I soon came to chambers which had dung charges in them. The very top one had a large white egg (shaped something like a short sausage) at the end nearest to the shaft leading from the hole in the dung. All the other chambers I could find were charged with dung but had no egg. However the beetles were present and presumably the female would soon have laid an egg on each charge of dung.

I pushed the dung charge with the egg into a 3 in. × 1 in. specimen tube and added some soil so as nearly to fill the tube. The soil and dung were quite moist. When I reached home I cut a number of grooves down the side of the cork so that it admitted air to the tube, which was placed on my desk. The egg duly hatched and the larva gradually ate the dung to become large and plump, assuming the shape of a fleshy **J**. The shape of the larvae of cockchafers, stag beetles and many other members of the Lamellicorn beetles is similar. My larva still fitted easily into the tube.

I am reasonably sure the larva would have turned into a pupa and finally into an adult, but I did not see this happen because I became occupied with other things and the tube was slipped into a drawer. The soil and the dung dried out, and when I looked at the tube some three months later the larva was dead.

If you wish to make fuller investigation of the life history, I suggest that you construct a sub-terranium as described in the appendix of the late Miss Lulham's book *An Introduction to Zoology through Nature Study*, published by

Macmillan. It is a book well worth obtaining whether you wish to make a sub-terranium or not.

WATER BOATMEN

Diet of Water Boatman (Notonecta and Corixa)

Obtain three or four of both these animals from a pond. Put the water boatmen each into a jam-jar about two-thirds full of the pond water and having some of the blackish mud from the bottom of the pond. Do the same for *Corixa* in other jam-jars. Leave the water to settle and the insects to get used to their novel situations. Then put three fresh water shrimps (*Gammarus pulex*) into each jar.

In a day or two you will probably find that the animals of one kind have killed and partly eaten their shrimp, whilst the other animals have not attacked them. Can you find out by observation whether these latter ones catch smaller crustaceans, or eat under-water plants, or are ' filter feeders ' living on microscopic animals and particles of decaying plants ? It will not be an easy task.

LIGHT COMPASS REACTION

Many insects maintain their direction by reference to the sun, or brightest part of the horizon. The insect moves so that it preserves a constant angle between its direction of motion and the sun. That this is so may sometimes easily be shown by making use of one of the larger ground beetles sometimes to be seen crossing roads, backyards and areas of bare ground.

Experiments to demonstrate that insects steer their course with reference to the sun

(1) You need an assistant and a mirror. The assistant must stand so that he cuts off the direct sunlight from the

insect, which will then, of course, be in the assistant's
shadow. Meanwhile the operator reflects the sun's rays
onto the insect, using the mirror for this purpose. It will
usually be found that the insect will change course, so that
the angle between its new line of direction and the rays

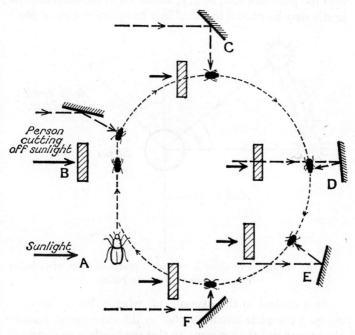

FIG. 15.—Light compass reaction (see text).

reflected from the mirror is approximately the same as it
previously was between the sun and the direction of motion.

Suppose you choose a beetle travelling at right angles to
the sun's rays (Fig. 15). If the operator first takes up such
a position that the reflected rays come from a direction only
a few degrees different from the original sun-rays, the beetle

can be induced to turn slightly to its right as in the diagram
(or, of course, to the left if the operator stands on the other
side of the assistant).

The assistant must move so that he keeps the beetle in his
shadow all the time. If the operator now gradually moves
into the positions B, C, D, E, F, as shown in the diagram, the
beetle may be caused to travel in a complete circuit of 360°.

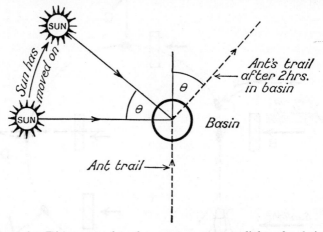

FIG. 16.—Diagram to show how an ant reacts to light, after being
hidden from it for two hours.

As a control to the experiment, when a beetle has gone
round a complete circuit of 360° in the experiment, remove
the mirror and the assistant, so that the beetle is again in full
sunlight. Note how he moves now.

(2) A simple observation is to pick up those caterpillars
and beetles which one sometimes sees pursuing a steady
course across a road in the bright sunlight, turn them round,
and replace them on the ground facing in the opposite
direction to that in which they were originally travelling.
In which direction do they now travel ?

(3) Ants near their nests travel along well-defined scent trails of formic acid. Away from the nest they often steer by the sun, and a most interesting experiment may be performed on such ants. Take an ordinary basin and place it over an ant which is travelling steadily in one direction. Mark the direction, by placing two sticks in the soil at a distance of a foot or so from each other. Make certain that the basin securely traps the ant. Leave the basin over the ant for about two hours; then remove it and mark the direction which the ant now takes. The angle between this new direction and the original direction of the ant's movement will be equal to the angle through which the sun's rays have moved in the interval (Fig. 16).

N.B. To find the angle through which the sun's rays have passed, a separate vertical stick should be set up and its shadow at the beginning of the experiment marked, either on the ground, or by a single stick near the end of the shadow. At the end of the experiment the new shadow should be marked in the same way, and the angle between the two shadows will be equal to the angle through which the sun's rays have passed during the experiment.

LEAF MINERS

It is inevitable that anyone with an interest in nature study will not go long before he meets with examples of leaf miners. In a garden there may very likely be leaf miners in the leaves of lilac and holly, in such weeds as sow-thistle, blackberry and dock and many others. The miners make a lighter patch on their area of the leaf, and if you try to remove the epidermis here you will find that it comes off readily on one side or the other of the leaf. Inside, in summer, there will usually be present one or more fairly mature insect larvae, though in leaves like holly which persist for several years the insects may have previously escaped, leaving a hole behind them.

Some of the insects (mainly two-winged flies and tiny moths, but also a few wasps and beetles) escape as larvae and complete their development outside the leaf mine, but others (such as *Phytomyza ilicis*, the two-winged fly in holly) complete their maturation in the leaf and escape only as adult insects. In these instances the pupal cases may be found, the one in holly looking like a flattened house-fly pupa, though much smaller. This fly attacks only holly, but many leaf miners can use a variety of plants.

A leaf mine is made as the larva gradually sweeps away the cells. The larva lies on its side and swishes to and fro with its mouth. It can be likened to a countryman with a scythe mowing corn, and very often a distinct pattern of arcs can be seen where it has devoured the cells.

One difficulty, because of the narrow space, is the disposal of the droppings. Some of the larvae, like the holly leaf larvae, distribute their droppings along a mid-line which continues throughout the mine; others, such as those in docks, place the droppings in a mass at one place. There are several larvae together in a dock leaf mine, but they all use the same dunging place.

There are several kinds of leaf mine shape (Plate IV, c). In several common plants (e.g. blackberry and sow-thistle), the mine starts as a narrow band which gradually widens out as the larva traverses a portion of the leaf. There are other shapes, that in the holly being an attenuated blotch, whilst that of the dock leaf insects is a great blotch which turns the affected part of the leaf a brown colour. There is very little known about leaf miners in wild plants, and no book of which I know is devoted to our British forms.

Find out by inspection whether leaf miners can eat across the larger veins. Look at a good number before coming to any decision. Also try to rear some of these insects. Remember that many types vacate their mines in order to complete their larval life, and then they pupate outside the leaf.

PLANT GALLS AND THEIR INHABITANTS

There awaits a stimulating field of research into those curious associations between plants and animals that we call galls. These galls are usually quite easy to find.

On a small oak tree growing in a hedgerow, and even on more mature trees, it should be possible to find marble galls, the little brown spherical balls about $\frac{3}{4}$ in. across the diameter. Examine these carefully in the autumn and find out if there are any tunnels opening on the surface. If the galls are very dark brown in colour very likely these tunnels will be present, perhaps only one, perhaps a dozen or so smaller ones, due to the escape of parasites of the original gall-forming grub. The holes show that the galls were made a year or two ago. If the galls are a lightish brown in colour and have no visible tunnels, then they very likely will have a curled-up white maggot in the centre. Careful opening with a knife will soon decide that issue.

Rearing insects from galls

(1) The adult insects emerge in September and October. To rear some of them, collect a number of galls in August, and place six or seven in each of several jam-jars. The mouth of each jar should be closed with a fine cloth, secured either with string or rubber bands. Look at the jars from time to time, say every two days, until the adult insects are hatched. You should obtain specimens of the actual gall wasp, *Cynips kollari*, as well as parasites and inquilines (see below), which will be present in some of the marble galls.

All the actual gall wasps will be females, but there is a strong suspicion that there is another, and quite different, generation which contains both males and females.

(2) Another gall very interesting to keep in a jam-jar with a secured cloth cover is the bedeguar, the gall on wild roses that becomes more and more red, with a luxuriant growth of thin plant threads. The galls may be as much as two inches long and an inch in diameter. Collect several of these galls in late autumn and place them in jam-jars, one in each. In the fullness of time, that is in early spring, the insects hatch out, and frequently one has several kinds of insects besides the actual gall-former *Rhodites rosae*. The other insects are parasites, superparasites (that is secondary parasites which feed on the primary parasites) and inquilines —insects which seem to do no direct damage to the other insects present, but which live in the galls.

It is worth mentioning that we do not yet know a great deal about the manner in which galls are formed. They clearly are made by the host plant, and have remarkably constant forms. What causes the host plant to make galls is far from clear. In some cases no galls are made until the eggs of the gall insect hatch and larvae appear. The larvae seem to secrete auxins[1] which cause the cambium to speed up its divisions, but in accordance with a definite manner so that the gall is formed in the usual way. In other cases some auxin is probably injected into the host when the gall insect's eggs are deposited.

Galls are more common on trees, but you should find some on herbaceous plants. Perhaps the most common is that which occurs on the stem (terminal part) of ground ivy (*Nepeta hederacea*) due to a wasp called *Aulax glechomae*. These galls are very common indeed from June onwards as little green swellings on the stems. As the larvae develop

[1] Auxins are growth-regulating chemicals found in plants.

towards maturity the galls become tinged with red. The wasp remains as a pupa which persists in the gall through the winter, and the adult wasp emerges in May of the following year.

APHIDES

Ants and Aphides

If in summer you look at a twig covered with aphides you will probably find nothing but females without wings. They live with their probosces dug into the phloem of the twigs, and they are not easily moved when once settled. They remain motionless and from time to time kick off from the anus a little globule of liquid which we call honey-dew. This is formed because more fluid than they can manage goes into the aphides from the twigs. Hence it must be eliminated.

Now, if you look for a short time you will see ants (the black lawn ant, for example) travelling about the twig and pausing behind the aphides. With their antennae the ants stroke the sides of the aphides' bellies, and very often they receive no positive response. However, from time to time a feeding aphid solicited by an ant will produce the droplet of honey-dew and keep it at its anus instead of kicking it away. The ant brings its jaws to the globule and drinks it with avidity. Then it most likely passes on to another aphid.

To see this phenomenon at its best one should have a reasonable hand lens (say a $\times 5$) to use. This feeding is a common enough thing, but unless looked for is passed unnoticed because the creatures are so small. Whether the symbiotic action extends always to the ants building shelters for the aphides, or even taking the aphides into their nest, is a matter which requires more research.

How quickly do aphides reproduce?

During the months of June and July aphides reproduce rapidly. How may we obtain some idea of the rate?

Take a small bottle or a collecting tube between 2 and 3 in. long. Then select a twig from, let us say, a rose. The twig should have no aphides upon it, so it will require close scrutiny. Put the end 2 in. or so in the tube or bottle (wide-mouthed, of course). It should have a few small leaves at the terminal point.

Now obtain a fat aphid that was walking about on the infested part of the rose bush. Remember that aphides not moving are probably feeding and will have their probosces deeply embedded in the plant phloem. Brush her off carefully with a paint brush (the smaller the better) and transfer her to the twig in the tube or bottle. Put in the cork. To make sure there are no eggs hatching on the rose, place three apparently aphid-clear twigs each in a separate tube, insert the corks and keep them with the other.

Look at them all after twenty-four hours, and then after forty-eight hours, counting the young aphides which appear. You will probably be surprised.

Which end of an aphid is born first?

These summer aphides are born as small insects—they do not hatch from eggs. I once lost a bet to a blacksmith in Peterborough with whom I was staying. He had a delightful warm aquarium containing, among other tropical fishes, some guppies. Guppies are viviparous—that is they do not lay eggs but give birth to baby guppies. I said that the guppies would be born head first, the obvious streamlined way. We watched the aquarium (guppies breed very freely) and soon my bet was lost. I may add that as a boy I was intrigued to find out which end of a hen's egg was delivered first. Finally, I watched a hen in a nesting box actually lay an egg, and so received an answer to my unspoken question. These experiences should help to hammer home the necessity for observations on each individual species. To answer the aphid question you must observe a number being born. That is easy enough in summer if you have a reasonable hand lens. I shall leave you to find out about the hen's egg yourself (but even an egg is occasionally laid with the 'wrong' end first).

ANTS

Guests in ants nests

Colonies of ants frequently have a variety of other creatures living with them as ' guests ' in their nests. These include beetles, various small wasps (*Hymenoptera*), two-winged flies, aphides, plant bugs (*Hemiptera heteroptera*), millipedes, false-scorpions (*Chelifer*) and the blind white woodlouse (*Platyarthrus hoffmanseggii*). Some of these ' guests ' may be discovered merely by opening up a small nest with a trowel, but a better method is to dig up the nest with a spade and throw it onto a white sheet. For a few seconds there may not be much visible, but after that some ' guests ' should be seen as they commence to move.

It is not easy to say whether these ' guests ' are really guests in the sense that the ants give them hospitality (e.g. shelter and food)—and receive nothing in return. It may well be that the ' guests ' are really symbionts, which give something that the ants value—it may be no more than a smell pleasant to the ants—in return for the favours they receive, so that both organisms profit from the association. Such an association with mutual profit is called symbiosis.

Defences of the Red Wood Ant (*Formica rufa*)

The popular belief that all ants can sting is incorrect. In many ants the sting is vestigial. Nevertheless, such forms do produce poison (formic acid) and this is sprayed over the object of attack. Some of the stingless ants first inflict a wound with their mandibles and then squirt the poison into the wound. The spraying effect can be well observed in the red wood ants, which live in large nests.

These nests, which may be several feet long and two to three feet high, are frequently built of pine needles or other vegetable detritus. They are common in the south, but are found sporadically almost to the Scottish border, and again are common in some Scottish areas. The mounds are generally on sandy heather; in oakwoods; and sometimes pinewoods. If such a nest is disturbed, many of the workers, raising themselves to do so, will discharge a clearly visible spray of formic acid from the end of the gaster (abdomen) and soon a heavy smell of formic acid will fill the air about the nest. One's face and hands should be kept at a safe distance from the nest. A discharge of formic acid into one's eyes would be extremely painful. These ants find tobacco smoke particularly irritating.

It has been claimed that a red wood ant lived for twenty-nine days without its head. The experiment could be repeated in a simple manner by enclosing a decapitated ant in a corked specimen tube (or aspirin tube) with a little damp cotton wool to keep the atmosphere inside the tube saturated.

BUTTERFLIES AND MOTHS

Butterflies and birds

Butterflies are often attacked by birds, which seize the insect by the wings. Frequently the birds release the butterflies, either intentionally because they are distasteful, or accidentally when changing their grip. If as many butterflies as possible are caught and examined, particularly old and tattered specimens, one may find a specimen whose wings (or wing) clearly show the mark of a bird's beak.

The white butterflies are presumably distasteful to birds, for they are seldom attacked, even when an attack would seem to offer every chance of success. I have seen a cabbage white attacked on the wing by a sparrow, but the butterfly eluded the bird and escaped. Possibly this was a young bird.

Butterflies and flight

One frequently catches specimens of butterflies whose wings are badly tattered. The flight of these seems to be in no way impeded.

Catch butterflies and clip their wings with scissors, to find out how much clipping of the outer portions of the wings does impair the power of flight. Confine your activities to one common species (e.g. the meadow brown), and do your observations outside, where the butterflies are numerous.

The hind wings of many moths are attached firmly to the front wings during flight. The same is true of the wings of bees and wasps. In butterflies there is no actual attachment of the hind wing to the front wing, but there is a stiffened portion or lobe on the front edge of the hind wing near its attachment to the body. This presumably supports the front wing during flight. Find if there is any effect if this is removed first from one hind wing and then from both.

The treated butterflies in these experiments are best liberated in a place (e.g. centre of a field) where they may be recaptured and several observations made if desired on their powers of flight.

F

Colour recognition in butterflies

Do butterflies recognise one another by sight ? This topic has been fairly completely investigated, for some species, by Eltringham and Ford, whose work suggests these experiments. (I have not yet carried them out myself.)

Obtain several dead specimens of the small tortoiseshell, or if it is late in the year, of the red admiral or peacock butterfly. Choose a hot sunny day on which the butterflies are flying freely. Place a dead open specimen of the chosen species on a piece of white cardboard and cover it with a sheet of glass. Have the inside of the wings facing upwards. Then place it with the cardboard in contact with the ground a few feet away from flowers known to be visited by members of that species. Place a similar sheet of cardboard, covered with glass, but without the butterfly, in a suitable position near the flowers, but not too near the experimental card.

Keep watch to find out whether flying butterflies ' dip ' towards the cards as they pass over them. If they do ' dip ' towards the card with the butterfly on it, and not to the one without, it may be argued that it is because the dead insect gives off some scent which is attractive to other members of the species.

This point may easily be settled.

From thin white cardboard (e.g. postcard), or cartridge paper, cut out flat shapes of the butterfly being studied. Leave one as it is, and colour another with paints as accurately as possible in the natural colours. Colour two other shapes in patterns markedly different from the insect being studied, but utilise the same colours. Now place the four paper models under glass as before, at equal distances from one another around the chosen plant, and observe the reactions of flying butterflies.

To eliminate the objection that the position occupied by

a particular model may be more or less favourable than that occupied by another, change the positions at suitable intervals.

Sex recognition in butterflies

If you have a setting board, set three male and three female small cabbage whites. In a few days they will be rigid and can be pinned into corks. If you do not possess a board you can spread out the butterflies (back surface upwards) on a piece of cork and keep the wings displayed by strips of cardboard and pins. A pin must pierce the thorax of each butterfly to hold it down on the cork. Place them on the ground but conveniently in your field of view and see what happens.

Make a list of the butterflies, A, B, C being the females, D, E, F the males. Make a tick on the list each time a particular dried specimen is investigated by another small cabbage white. Which set, the males or females, receive more attention ?

Caterpillar prolegs

Obtain a large caterpillar. Hold it so that the soles of its prolegs (cushion feet) are upwards, and examine one of these through a strong hand lens. The row (or rows) of tiny ' hooks ' will be visible, and usually, in a lively caterpillar, the manner in which they obtain a foothold for the caterpillar will be seen.

Selection of food plant by caterpillars

When collecting insects in long herbage by means of a sweep net, one frequently obtains several caterpillars in addition to grasshoppers, beetles, and many other insects, as well as spiders and harvestmen. Usually it is not easy to identify the caterpillars, and often the simplest way to do so is to rear them until the adult moths hatch out.

To do this you have to feed each caterpillar upon its proper food plant (or plants). But if the name of the caterpillar is not known, you cannot find the name of the food plant from books, which is the usual procedure.

The correct food plant may usually be found as follows: Collect small samples of several of the most likely plants and place them in a jam-pot, together with the caterpillar. Cover the mouth of the jam-pot with a piece of muslin. Leave the caterpillar for two or three hours. At the end of this period inspect the pot, and often the caterpillar will be seen to be feeding on one of the leaves. This will be its food plant.

Should the caterpillar not be feeding, but be wandering disconsolately around the pot, the probability is that the food plant is not included in the collection. One must then make a further collection of plants not included in the first batch, and try again.

When the food plant has been discovered in this way, one should search for a specimen in flower. Its name may then be found from a standard flora.[1] When the name of the food plant is known, one can hunt through appropriate books to find which caterpillars feed on the particular plants, and in this way the name of the caterpillar can be narrowed to one of a small number. Which of these the caterpillar under observation happens to be can usually be fairly easily settled by reference to written descriptions.

[1] If you are unable to use a proper flora, the coloured pictures in *A Flower Book for the Pocket*, by Skene (Oxford), are usually good enough, though this book will not help with the grasses. For these you will probably find help in the Penguin book, *Grasses*, by W. E. Hubbard.

Cocoon formation

The caterpillars of many moths form a cocoon, or protective case, around themselves before they pupate. The cocoon may be entirely of silk (e.g. silkworm), or it may be that silken threads are used to bind together hairs from the caterpillar. Sometimes other materials, leaves and small pieces of wood, are incorporated. Many of the moth caterpillars that pupate below ground (e.g. the *Noctuidae*) form an earthen cell by cementing soil particles together with a fluid secreted for that purpose.

If you can obtain several caterpillars of a species that spins a cocoon, experiments can be performed to determine whether the caterpillar will pupate before the cocoon is completed. (Silkworm moths are suitable for this purpose.) When the caterpillars are ready to spin, house them in separate tins or boxes which are fitted with detachable lids. As the cocoon nears completion cut a ' window ' in it with sharp scissors, using a pair of fine forceps to help the operation. Great care must be taken not to injure the caterpillar, which should be left undisturbed to give it an opportunity to repair the damaged cocoon if it is so disposed. If it does—it may take 6–12 hours—cut away another piece. Continue doing this and find out whether ultimately the caterpillar will pupate with a hole in the wall of its cocoon. Meanwhile the control caterpillars will have pupated.

Orange-tip butterfly caterpillars

When I wish to find the eggs of the orange-tip butterfly, I search on the flower stems of jack-by-the-hedge (sometimes called hedge mustard). Usually the eggs are found singly just beneath the flowers, but occasionally they are lower down on the main stem. When freshly laid, the eggs are whitish-yellow, but they gradually turn to rich orange and, just before hatching, to a purplish colour. The caterpillars are coloured greenish-blue, and they feed on the developing fruit (siliquas).

One year I fed about 20 caterpillars. Each was on the end of a sprig of jack-by-the-hedge which dipped into an 8-oz. medicine bottle filled with water. The sprig was plugged into the bottle with cotton wool. The bottles with their sprays and caterpillars made a row across my mantel-piece (on newspaper, of course, so that my wife did not complain of the droppings!) and the caterpillar grew merrily in size.

Then, at the end of June, they began to disappear. I was out all day and in the garden in the evenings, and I could not for the life of me make out where the caterpillars went. Why did they not pupate on their food plant ? Finally there was but one left. It was a Saturday afternoon, and I was marking examination papers. I had been looking at the orange-tip caterpillar and I rested the bottle on the table in front of me.

I looked at it some while afterwards, and to my surprise it was beginning to pupate on the plant. I watched it for a long time. It already had a little silky mat which its anal claspers grasped. Its head end pointed upwards and it was busy, spinning the girdle, moving its head from side to side producing the silk. Finally it lay still, and in a while the front part split along the back, revealing the new pupa. Gradually the old skin was detached by shaking, and it slipped downwards and off, leaving an arc-shaped pupa (Plate IV).

This was my only success, as I have said, and I decided to read the facts. It seems that orange-tip caterpillars in England normally desert their rather frail food plants and pupate on more rigid plants. They cannot, of course, know as we can that the food plants are not sturdy enough to remain erect through a usual winter. Why do they go? Note that some books are not quite correct on this subject.

Is its own egg case the first meal of a Large Cabbage White butterfly caterpillar?

You will probably know that there are two broods of this butterfly, the first brood being on the wing in late May and June, whilst the other brood, from the eggs laid by the first, are not seen until late August and September. The butterflies in this second brood are much more numerous than in the spring brood, and this means that more eggs are laid in the autumn. Consequently I advise you to carry out these observations then.

You will need a batch of eggs. It is possible to watch for large cabbage whites visiting the main food plants—members of the cabbage family and nasturtiums. If a butterfly alights and remains more or less hidden for some while, she has probably laid eggs. With perseverance and some luck you may actually watch her lay her eggs. One I watched had gripped the edge of a nasturtium leaf with her front legs and her head was visible. Under the leaf her abdomen pressed against the lower surface and then dropped down, leaving a golden yellow egg cemented to the leaf. In a few seconds she raised her abdomen and quickly another egg was cemented against the first. This was continued for several minutes, and then she flew away leaving a patch of eggs—I counted fifty-eight—looking like tiny yellow milk bottles all touching one another, and all firmly cemented to the leaf. With a hand lens the eggs could be seen to have delicate ridges running down from the top to the base. With a powerful hand lens ($\times$ 20) I was able to see delicate cross bars linking the ribs.

If you do not have the luck to see a large cabbage white laying eggs, you will have to search for the conspicuous yellow egg clusters among the nasturtiums, or turn over the leaves of cabbages, purple sprouting broccoli, and other members of the cabbage group of plants. The egg clusters are laid underneath the leaves, and so are not easy to find.

When you obtain your batch of eggs you can take the leaf on which the eggs occur and cut it with scissors, so that it will fit into a 3 in. × 1 in. specimen tube, then put in the cork and place the tube on the mantelpiece, or anywhere else in the light where you can look at it frequently. There is no need to admit oxygen, for the eggs consume very little. In any case the green leaf will every day restore oxygen to the air in the tube by the process of photosynthesis. You will find that the leaf remains quite firm.

The eggs are at first a golden yellow. As the time of hatching approaches the eggs darken, and then finally the tops of the eggs become very dark whilst the lower parts are a creamy yellow. With suitable lighting you should be able (with a hand lens) to see the caterpillars moving in their egg-shells, and quite soon they will begin to hatch. If you look at your eggs every half-hour you are certain to catch some caterpillars hatching. It takes only a minute or two for a caterpillar to push its way out of its egg-shell, once it has breached the wall. The empty egg-shell is now a creamy light grey, and you will soon know whether the caterpillar wanders away from it, or turns to it and eats it. You cannot, of course, assume that different kinds of butterfly caterpillars act in the same way. Each will have to be investigated separately.

Large Cabbage White butterfly pupae on walls: are they vulnerable to birds?

The caterpillars of the large cabbage white butterfly expose themselves quite openly on their food plants, and I think that their yellow and black stripes act as a warning coloration to birds. Certainly, birds do not seem to molest them, as they so easily could. But what happens to the caterpillar after it has turned into a pupa (or chrysalis, as some prefer to call it)?

From time to time you will come across a wall that borders a vegetable or flower garden. It may be the wall of a house, a garden wall, or even the walls of a shed. If the food plants of the cabbage white are present in the garden, and the gardener has not made ruthless warfare against the caterpillars, you will very likely in October be able to see caterpillars climbing the walls, and when they are well off the ground they will pupate. I have found that they are partial to some outpointing ledge — frequently under the coping stones of the wall. I discovered one pupating under the top bar of the gate of my poultry run this very evening, just before I wrote this; the caterpillar must have travelled

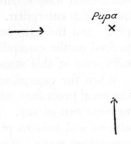

FIG. 17.—Means of indicating the position of a pupa on a wall.

across the ground for a full twenty yards from its cabbage. Some caterpillars will pupate on the surface of the wall, without any apparent protection from either weather or bird.

Are the pupae eaten by birds? During late October, mark on some sort of wall the position of a number of pupae, using white chalk. For each selected pupa draw two arrows at right angles to each other, and in such a way that, were the arrows extended, the point of intersection would be at the site of the pupa. The arrows will help you to find the pupae, or discover their absence, without a lot of searching (Fig. 17).

Look week by week at the pupae and keep a record of how long they remain there.

To what extent are the caterpillars of the Large Cabbage White butterfly parasitised by the ichneumon wasp (Apanteles glomeratus)?

The caterpillars of the large cabbage white butterfly do not always manage to pupate. This is because, during their feeding stage, the caterpillars have been attacked by a small ichneumon wasp (*Apanteles glomeratus*), which lays its eggs inside the caterpillar. The eggs hatch inside the caterpillar, and the ichneumon larvae coming from them begin to feed on the caterpillar's tissues, but they do not kill the caterpillar at this stage.

When the caterpillar is ready to pupate it goes through the usual procedure, and will climb a suitable structure and weave a mat of silk. It is, however, rather sluggish in its actions and fails to produce the silk girdle which normal caterpillars make. Nor does its body noticably hump up, as does that of an unattacked caterpillar when a chrysalis is forming. Instead, its body wall breaks down and small greyish maggots come out of its body. These very quickly spin, each one for itself, a silken cocoon, primrose-yellow in colour. These cocoons are spun right against the caterpillar's body, which is not usually dead at that time and may live for a day or so after. The number of cocoons varies from perhaps ten to thirty (one I have just counted had seventeen in the heap) and the pile of cocoons is very conspicuous.

To make an estimation of the percentage of attack in your area, a suitable box with a rigid cover fitting flush will be required. I use a tall cardboard box in which the groceries are delivered, with two sheets of glass for the cover. Into your box put caterpillars from food plants in the garden. Choose caterpillars which look as if they are ready to pupate. This condition is not difficult to determine. Any caterpillar crawling across the soil or up any structure is certain to be about to pupate. If you want to be certain, place a sheet of newspaper on the floor of the box, and stand a bottle on this (a milk bottle is excellent) and put in two or three leaves of broccoli or cabbage (trimmed with scissors if necessary). Then place your caterpillars on these leaves. If they are not fully fed they will continue to eat. The droppings can be removed every two days or so with the paper, and fresh sheets of paper substituted. There is no need to put water into the bottle which contains the broccoli or cabbage leaves.

When all the caterpillars in your cage have pupated or produced ichneumon cocoons, it is easy enough to calculate the percentage attack. Make a written record, and see if the percentage varies much from year to year. It will be obvious to you that the more caterpillars you use the more reliable will be your results.

Does the colour of a Large Cabbage White pupa depend on the colour of the background where it pupates?

Take half a dozen 2-lb. jam-jars with lids and make bands of black, white, red, blue, yellow, and green paper so that the glass in each jar is covered except for a $\frac{1}{2}$ in. vertical slit to admit light. The lids are lined inside each with the colour of paper used on its jar, and each jar should stand on a piece of its paper. Some papers are coloured on one side only. In such a case the colour must face towards the interior of the jar.

Now get a number of large white caterpillars ready to pupate—as many as you can find—and place them in the jars as nearly as you can in equal numbers. The best way of getting a good supply of caterpillars is to rear them from eggs, using the food plant on which the eggs were laid. Then you will know that the caterpillars are from the same mother and have lived in the same environment, which gives a good control in the experiment. The control can never be complete, however, because the female butterfly mates several times, receiving male sex cells from all her mates. Hence, there will be several fathers represented in a brood of caterpillars, and it is possible that the progeny of different fathers may have different sensitivities to colour.

Another reason for rearing caterpillars from eggs is that large cabbage white caterpillars are frequently heavily parasitised by the ichneumon wasp, *Apanteles* (see p. 82), as many as 90 per cent of the caterpillars being parasitised in some areas. This high rate of parasitation may occur because the large cabbage white caterpillars live for some time as a fully exposed colony, usually under a leaf; but whatever the reason these ' wild ' caterpillars may spoil your experiment by failing to pupate. If you do rear your own, do so in a box which can be covered over with a fine cloth, e.g. muslin, to prevent the entry of the parasitic flies. In the experiment you require at least one chrysalis from each jam-jar so that you can compare the whole gamut of colour, but more specimens are highly desirable.

The experiment can be repeated with other common butterflies. The small tortoiseshell is easy to obtain, and its food plants are the perennial stinging nettle (*Urtica dioica*) and the annual stinging nettle (*Urtica urens*). The caterpillars usually leave the food plant in order to pupate, and the pupae vary a good deal in colour. I took a colour photograph of a pupa hanging from a leaf of hardheads (*Centaurea nigra*), and it had a remarkable golden sheen. This is a justification for using the alternative name of chrysalis for pupa, since the word chrysalis means ' a golden thing ', being derived from the Greek word *chrūsos*—gold.

However, not all small tortoiseshell chrysalides have this beautiful golden reflection, as no doubt you will discover.

The Ghost Moth (Hepialus humuli)

The white female ghost moths are on the wing at dusk on summer nights, darting here and there, remaining for a few moments and then—off again. The brownish-orange males tend to fly slowly and have the curious knack of disappearing from view by closing the wings, only to reappear when the wings are opened again. This is the reason they are called ghost moths.

The eggs are laid at the surface soil near to food plants such as burdock and dandelion, and the caterpillars feed upon the roots. I have found the large caterpillars in May and June in nests they have constructed right at the base of tussocks of cock's-foot grass, and they pupate just below.

Walk about the lanes or garden in the twilight of summer days to find out if the moths fly in your area. If they do (they are generally distributed) try the effect of pulling at tufts of cock's-foot grass on waste ground. Very likely you will be able to find several caterpillars not yet pupated. At least, that was my experience on the rough ground of my garden at Bakewell.

If there is no cock's-foot grass, try digging up white dead nettle clumps, or dandelions, in the hedgerow, and searching them for this caterpillar. When mature, it is about $1\frac{1}{2}$ in. long, plump, and mainly greyish with a few black spots. Recently I have been given two of these caterpillars, each living in a central tunnel it had eaten in a carrot.

SAWFLIES

Are the larvae of the pear-tree sawfly masked from birds?

When I was living near Tamworth, one year, towards the
end of September, many of the leaves of my cherry tree
became rather odd in appearance.   Their leaves had patches
of tissue eaten away to the lower epidermis.   I was digging
one day underneath a lowish branch of this cherry when
I noticed that each leaf had one, or sometimes two or sometimes three, small bird droppings on it (Plate VII, B).   I dug
a few more spadefuls of soil, thinking about these bird
droppings, and then I decided to examine them more
closely.   When I had reached a leaf and begun to examine
it I received a surprise, because the bird dropping on it
became active.   Then I realised what the ' bird droppings '
were.   It was quite easy to scrape off the black slime or
jelly from one, to reveal the caterpillar of a pear-tree sawfly,
which had been living on the leaf, but inside its own covering.
Each apparent bird dropping was quite realistic.   The
covering of the sawfly was jet black, but it could easily be
rubbed off.   The deception of bird dropping was increased
by a conspicuous swelling behind the caterpillar's head,
and the fact that the head was held up slightly from the leaf
on which the ' dropping ' rested (Plate VII, B).   Why these
caterpillars were on the cherry was a puzzle to me, for there
were pear trees quite close to it.

The appearance and behaviour of these caterpillars
strongly suggested that they were trying to hide their body
from attack by birds.   In other words, these sawflies are
probably, in the larval state, palatable to birds.   If you
can find some of these pear-tree sawfly caterpillars, try the
effect of removing the black coating and offering the caterpillars to birds such as hens, budgerigars or canaries.   Other
sawflies, such as the one which attacks gooseberry bushes,

are not palatable to birds, and they advertise this by being brightly coloured and by feeding openly in the daytime.

BEES

Do bees start at the bottom of the inflorescence?

In the majority of insect-pollinated flowers the stamens ripen before the stigmas, so that a particular flower will dust pollen onto a visiting insect for some time before its stigma is receptive to pollen.

Many flowering plants have the spike or raceme type of inflorescence, where individual flowers are arranged along the length of a more or less vertical stem, and of these flowers the lower ones open first. Frequently, indeed, the petals of the lower flowers will have dropped before the top flowers are open. This is so in lupins, hollyhocks and rose bay willow-herb (*Chamaenerion angustifolium*).

If an insect visited a hollyhock, say, and commenced with the young flowers at the top of the spike it would get dusted with pollen from these because their stamens would be ripe. The stigmas of these flowers are not yet receptive and no pollen would be deposited on them. As the insect worked its way down the spike it would come sooner or later to older flowers whose stigmas are ripe. These stigmas would be dusted with pollen from the insect, but this pollen would most likely be pollen that the insect had just received from the flowers higher on the same plant.

If the insect started at the bottom of the inflorescence and worked its way up, however, it would first encounter those flowers which had receptive stigmas and whose pollen was for the most part already gone. Should the insect be carrying pollen from another flower, as would be likely, this would be the pollen to be deposited on the stigmas, thus bringing about the cross-pollination with another plant of the same species. Such cross-pollination is usually held to be more advantageous than self-pollination. It is worth remarking that whatever may be the behaviour of the insects in this connection, it is not within the power of the plant to control it.

Settle, by observation of suitable plants, these points:

(1) Do bees (hive or bumble) methodically work in one direction up or down either a long inflorescence, or in suitable cases (e.g. climbing geranium), an entire plant ?

(2) If so, is the direction of working from the base towards the apex, or vice versa ?

(3) Is the plant under observation protandrous (i.e. do the stamens ripen and shed their pollen before the stigma is receptive) ?

(4) Do bumble bees ' working ' nasturtiums ever enter a flower twice within a few minutes ?

Bees and flower constancy

It is often stated that hive bees are such valuable pollinating agents because they collect nectar and pollen from one kind of flower only, on particular visits. If you stand in the garden and watch, generally you will see that bees do, in fact, generally restrict their attention to one kind of flower. This ' flower constancy ' may last for several hours, even for one or more days, though of course different bees from a hive may work different flowers. One may restrict its visits to, say, a sycamore tree, while another works only a particular patch of hawthorn. Some years hawthorn is not worked by bees; presumably its nectar is weak, or even absent. The flowers are worth examining in such a year.

Do bumble bees show the same flower constancy as hive bees ?

This question may most readily be settled by watching bumble bees in a well-stocked flower garden or in a country lane where there are many varieties of flowers.

A different method is to catch a bumble bee which is carrying loads of pollen on its hind legs. The pollen is carried in special pollen baskets, and the manner of filling the pollen baskets is such that the first pollen collected is ultimately found at the top of the pollen basket, while the last pollen to be added is at the bottom. If a hind leg bearing pollen is detached from a dead bumble bee, and a longitudinal cut made through the pollen mass (and leg if possible) with a razor, it is easy to see if various colours and shapes of pollen are present. If they are, it is clear evidence that the bee has visited different flowers. Does the type of land, e.g. house gardens, country lanes, or heather moors, have any influence?

You may possibly find that in the pollen loads of hive bees also there are several pollens, but this is not so common.

Is the pollen in the pollen loads of bees stuck together with some sticky substance, or merely packed in tightly?

This is easily determined from the hind leg of a laden bee, the bee having been made insensible in a laurel-leaf killing bottle. Do you think honey or nectar might be used? If you have a microscope available see if the pollen grains are sculptured or smooth. Sculpturing on the grains would help them to cohere, and this would be assisted if the grains were covered with honey or nectar.

Do hive bees pollinate buttercups?

Buttercups are usually pollinated by short-tongued insects (e.g. certain flies and beetles). Hive bees normally avoid visiting buttercup flowers just as cows avoid buttercup foliage. In hard seasons you may see hive bees visiting the buttercups. Can you find out by observation whether they seek nectar or pollen or both?

G

Do hive bees ever collect pollen from wind-pollinated flowers?

My answer to this is that they do, for in certain seasons my bees used to swarm among the flowers of a wych elm (*Ulmus glabra*) in my garden. The tree flowered in late February or early March, when there were not many other flowers about. Some branches of the wych elm bent down to within seven feet of the ground, and I was able to obtain a good view of the bees collecting pollen.

You might watch some other early wind-pollinated plants such as dog's mercury (*Mercurialis perennis*), hazel (*Coryllus avellana*) and alder (*Alnus glutinosa*).

GRASSHOPPERS

Grasshopper exhaustion

Most of our British grasshoppers are coloured in such a way that, if they remain motionless in their normal habitat, they are amazingly difficult to see. This fact will probably have been verified many times by the reader when he has been out collecting. One notices a grasshopper in the grass, makes a move to catch it when—click! and it has gone. Further search for it is usually quite futile.

The escape mechanism consists in one quick leap to a distance of several feet, followed by immobility. The leap is made so suddenly that the eye fails to follow the flight of the grasshopper. Further movement by the grasshopper, after the initial leap, would be worse than useless as it would betray its whereabouts. One leap must normally be quite sufficient to escape from enemies. Hence one is tempted to wonder as to the stamina of grasshoppers. How often can they jump without becoming exhausted?

The question can be settled by obtaining one or two un-damaged specimens (they may be obtained by ' sweeping ' meadows or other long herbage in the summer) and taking them to a piece of bare ground where there is no cover—a roadway or pavement, concrete yard, or even the floor of a room. Liberate a grasshopper from its container and, if it does not at once jump of its own volition, cause it to jump by touching it. Normally it will be easy enough to see where it lands. Make it jump again—and again—and again. Do its leaps get more feeble ? In addition, does the insect become more reluctant to jump again after each leap ? Can you so exhaust the insect that it can make only the feeblest attempt to jump even when stimulated strongly, as by tobacco smoke ?

When you have an apparently exhausted grasshopper, find out if its leaping power is regained after a few minutes' rest.

Does a grasshopper always jump in the same direction?

To answer this question one needs a few undamaged grasshoppers, and a bare floor space (concrete or asphalt yard, or a suitable room).

Obtain a rectangle (about 12 in. × 9 in.) of stiff white paper, and mark the mid-points of the long sides A and B respectively with an ink dot. Draw a pencil line from A to B.

Place the grasshopper on the floor and wait until it is resting quietly. Then advance the rectangle so that the line AB points along the long axis of the grasshopper's body with the point A nearest to the grasshopper. Now advance the paper until the point A makes contact with the grasshopper and causes it to jump. Hold the paper in position and with a pencil make a dot (C) on the paper so that C, A, and the midpoint of the grasshopper's body (as you can see it) are in a straight line. Connect A and C with a pencil line (Fig. 18).

Repeat the experiment a number of times, and it will be

obvious after, say, ten trials, whether the grasshopper always jumps in one direction or not.   Always touch it in the same place to make it jump.

When you are satisfied with this experiment, find out if

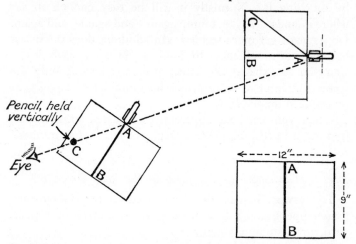

FIG. 18.   To determine the direction in which a grasshopper jumps.

a grasshopper is liable to jump in different directions if it is touched in different places.   Place the grasshopper on a short line (1 in.) in the centre of a piece of white paper, and put its direction of jumping onto the paper, drawing this direction from the centre of the line, and writing on it the direction of the particular stimulus.   It will be enough if you give stimuli from (1) the anterior, (2) the left thoracic side, (3) the posterior of the abdomen, (4) the right thoracic side.   The stimuli may be applied with a thin twig.

Do all grasshoppers of the same species jump in the same direction ?

To do this carry out the above experiment on, say, five

different members of a grasshopper species but stimulating each grasshopper from the posterior end of the abdomen. Compare the results you obtain.

LACEWINGS

Eggs of green lacewing

When I originally took the photograph (Plate V, A) of a hawthorn branch bearing, on a leaf, a cluster of white eggs, each egg at the end of a white stalk, I was completely unable to identify the eggs. I thought it was a curious way for the eggs to be laid, projecting downwards into the air. By searching through relevant books I was finally able to identify the eggs as those laid by a particular lacewing fly.

In time, larvae hatched from the eggs, and gained the under-surface of the hawthorn leaf. Then they moved along the leaf stalk and onto the twig, where there were dense clusters of aphids. They began to eat these at once.

You may be wondering what is the purpose of the thread holding the eggs separately in the air. Could it be that there would be cannibalism if the eggs were touching? That is, would the first hatched larva eat unhatched cells? Alternatively, would the young larvae attack one another? I leave you to find this out by experimenting on clusters of eggs. One way of obtaining information would be to cut all the eggs of a cluster from their stalks, and put them in a small vertical test-tube, afterwards inserting a cork. There will be ample oxygen for the eggs to hatch and for the young larvae to live, if they do not kill one another.

In certain species of lacewings the pedicels bearing the eggs are tangled together mid-way along their length. Do you think the newly-hatched larvae here are likely to eat one another? It may take you several years to solve this problem, because, of course, you will have to find out if all the eggs hatch together.

CHAPTER FOUR

VERTEBRATE ANIMALS

FROGS

An experiment with frog spawn

Various functions are attributed to the jelly surrounding the eggs of frogs. It is held to protect the eggs from being eaten by waterfowl and fishes, the argument being that these creatures, who cannot eat a whole mass of spawn at once, find it difficult, or impossible, to detach small pieces from the mass. Another function of the jelly may be to space out the eggs so that they are separated from one another by a certain minimum distance, and so each egg will have a better chance of obtaining oxygen than if they were all packed tightly together. It is certainly true that developing eggs require plenty of oxygen, and it is also true that if frog spawn is packed into a jam-pot so as to fill it, the spawn underneath very quickly dies. That at the surface lives for a considerably longer time, and if removed from the decomposing mass of the remainder may continue to develop.

Frog spawn when freshly laid sinks to the bottom of the water. In a few days when the jelly has swelled by absorbing water, the spawn rises to the surface. Spawn tested by me on one occasion, however (15.3.49), did not rise to the surface, although it developed; and I have several times since found spawn on the floor of ponds, spawn which showed no inclination to float to the top.

The surface of the water is a favourable situation for the development of eggs because there is a good supply of oxygen and the temperature may be considerably higher than it is deeper down in the water. The question arises, 'May it not be an important function of the jelly to raise the inert eggs to the surface and to support them there during development?' In other words, would the developing eggs sink to the bottom if deprived of the support of the buoyant jelly?

This question may easily be settled by dissecting several eggs from their containing jelly, and placing them in water to discover whether they sink or float. The dissection is easily done by placing a sample of spawn on several thicknesses of newspaper. It is then a simple matter to separate an egg from its jelly by means of a needle and scalpel (or pen-knife). The egg will be found to be quite sticky, and difficult to remove from the paper. The simplest method of transferring it to water is to tear off the portion of the newspaper on which it rests and dip the paper under the water to which it is desired to transfer the egg. The egg may then be easily brushed into the water.

Several eggs should be tested at once, and the experiment repeated at intervals during the fortnight or so between the laying of the eggs and their hatching.

The effect on tadpoles of a meat diet as compared with a vegetable diet

The effect on growth of a diet rich in protein may be investigated, using frog tadpoles.

Find a mass of frog spawn floating at the surface of a pond. The eggs in this mass will, of course, have been fertilised. When the tadpoles hatch, feed them on vegetable matter (e.g. raw carrot, cabbage leaves and similar substances) for four or five weeks. Do they eat every kind of water plant offered to them?

Obtain two suitable containers (e.g. small aquaria)—but failing these any reasonably large bowl or bucket that will house ten tadpoles. Place ten tadpoles in water in one container, and feed these on vegetable matter. Place another ten tadpoles in water in the second container. Feed these on raw meat. If no other suitable meat is available, short pieces of chopped earthworm will serve admirably, but do not allow the water in the container to become foul. At the first sign of turbidity change it for fresh. Do not allow pieces of earthworm or meat to lie on the bottom; attach each to a length of cotton, which should be placed to enable you to withdraw the meat when you deem it advisable.

If the tadpoles fed on meat are compared after about a month with the controls that have been fed on vegetable matter, a striking difference in size will be apparent. Which group turns into frogs first?

HOW ANIMALS LEARN

Trial and error learning by chickens

Many creatures (including man) learn by making mistakes. This type of learning is easy to demonstrate in young chickens, three or four days old. Take a board about two feet square (or a sheet of stout brown paper will do) and glue to it thirty or forty cabbage seeds, scattered at random over the paper. Any kind of quick-setting household glue will serve for this purpose.

Next it is necessary to demonstrate that your chicks will eat both cabbage seeds and lettuce seeds. This may easily be done by presenting them with a mixture of a few cabbage and lettuce seeds. It is likely that they will readily peck at, and eat, both kinds.

When you are satisfied that the chicks do eat both types of seeds, take the board (or brown paper) with the cabbage seeds fixed to it, and sprinkle on it some lettuce seeds, which are of a different colour, shape and size, from cabbage. Offer the board to the chicks and allow them plenty of time (say half an hour) to peck freely. At the end of this time the lettuce seeds will all have been eaten, but the cabbage seeds, since they are firmly fixed to the board, will remain.

In about an hour, repeat the process. Sprinkle another batch of lettuce seeds onto the board and offer it to the chicks again for a short time. Do this several more times, and finally offer to the chicks a new mixture of loose cabbage and lettuce seeds. It is likely that they will eat the lettuce but make no attempt to eat the cabbage. They have learned, by trial and error, that cabbage seeds are stuck to the substrate and that they cannot be dislodged, hence it is no use pecking at them.

Chicks do not peck at objects which they have found to be useless as food, and so do not try to pick up the cabbage seeds, although these are now loose and could be eaten. One is reminded of the account of the man who set up a stall in London and offered to sell gold sovereigns for three-pence each. He did a very poor trade, because people had learned, by trial and error (experience), that bargains are deceptive, that folks do not sell valuable goods at a fraction of their worth.

Habituation to a stimulus by nestlings (extinction of a response)

Find a nest of some nidicolous[1] bird such as the black-bird or thrush with nestlings whose eyes are not yet opened. When the parent birds are away from the nest gently agitate it to imitate the effect of one of the parents alighting on it. Usually the nestlings will at once respond by stretching

[1] Birds whose eggs hatch into very immature nestlings, naked and with eyes unopened, which complete their development in the nest.

their necks upwards and opening their enormous gapes in an expectant manner.

In a few seconds, if no food is forthcoming and no further movement of the nest takes place, the nestlings will settle down again. When they have done so, agitate the nest a second time. Once more wait until they have settled and then repeat the agitation. Go on doing this until the nestlings no longer respond, i.e. until they have learned that the particular type of agitation is not followed by food being placed in their beaks. We say that the nestlings are 'habituated' to this particular stimulus, meaning that they have come to ignore it because they have learned that it has no significance for them.

Habituation is one method of learning. Animals respond to stimuli which normally have some kind of significance, i.e. are followed by some kind of effect either beneficial or harmful to the organism concerned. If a stimulus is not followed by the normal sequel the animal's response to it the next time it occurs is weaker, and continues to grow weaker and weaker until it dies away entirely. The animal is then completely habituated. One sees this clearly when hens are introduced into a new pen to which a dog also has access. At first they respond by violent flutterings when the dog passes, but in a few days they no longer take any notice. They have become habituated, or, as we say, used to the dog.

Will nestlings swallow any material placed in the beak, i.e. do they trust the parent?

Offer *small* pieces of bacon rind, cheese and *small* pellets of moistened newspaper or cork to the nestlings and see how they react. The parents, of course, would never offer such unpalatable and useless matter as cork or moistened newspaper pellets.

Some animals learn that man is dangerous

The weaker wild creatures are quick to learn what is dangerous; if they failed to do so they would soon be exterminated. For some species man spells danger. On a rural walk you may occasionally see a pigeon or crow which was flying towards you suddenly swerve and make a detour. Pigeons and crows have learned to associate danger with man. Some countrymen believe that certain pigeons and crows can distinguish between a man with a gun and one without. Certainly some pigeons will continue to fly directly over one's head if one has not a gun. Such birds may sometimes be caused to swerve violently if one levels a walking stick or even just the arm at them in imitation of a gun; but remember that young birds may have had no experience of gunfire, and they may not take 'avoiding action'.

There is a poem by John Drinkwater called *Pike Pool* which has always appealed strongly to me. The first verse reads as follows:

> Down Beresford Dale, on my June birthday,
> When the dipper's brood had flown,
> In sixteen-hundred-and-seventy, say,
> Charles Cotton walked alone,
> And little Dove shone upon his muse,
> All babbling bright and cool,
> When sudden the world was wild with news—
> 'The Mayfly's on Pike Pool'.

Mayflies are possibly the choicest food a trout can desire and a good hatch throws the trout into a frenzied orgy. Pike Pool is a deep silent pool in the Derbyshire river Dove, which flows through Beresford Dale to Dove Dale. The pool is surrounded by trees, and from it rises a thin spike of rock, twenty to thirty feet high. This water was fished by Izaac Walton, the famous author of *The Compleat Angler*, in company with Charles Cotton, who owned the land. The Fishing Temple he built survives quite near the pool. I once had the good fortune to be invited to a day's fishing in Beresford Dale, but alas! not in mayfly time.

The day I went the fishing was good. I had a Wickham's Fancy (dry fly) on my line, and when I came to Pike Pool my very first cast placed the fly within a yard of the Pike. The water here was dark and looked unpromising but my heart missed a beat when an enormous trout—four pounds if an ounce—rose slowly from the silent depths towards my fly. I could swear that after inspecting the fly he looked warily at me, before laughing a fishy laugh to himself and sinking back out of sight. I made, in desperation, many more casts and changed to different flies, but I am sure that he had learnt that flies such as mine were to be avoided, and that anglers were enemies no doubt somehow connected with flies. I realise that this is non-scientific speculation, but it is a fact that small trout are caught very easily. They are returned to the water, and have presumably learned some sort of lesson. They may be caught again and again as little ones, but as they grow larger they seem to learn that danger is associated with artificial flies; perhaps it is the hook in them. I have often wondered whether one would get more ' rises ' if one fished with a fly from which the hook was cut off on the shank instead of with a fully barbed hook, but I have never been able to persuade myself to use good fishing time for such an experiment.

It seems also to be true that coarse fish, roach, bream, chub and so on, are much more difficult to catch now (at least the sizeable ones) than they were even fifty years ago. Read Izaac Walton's *Compleat Angler* if you are interested, and, if you get a chance, talk with aged anglers. I am speaking, of course, of unpolluted waters—many polluted rivers have few fish in them.

PROTECTIVE COLORATION

(1) CRYPTIC COLORATION. Most of the smaller animals have enemies which prey upon them, and many of them are coloured in such a way that when they are motionless they are difficult to see against their normal background. Such colouring is said to be *cryptic* (Greek *krupto* = hide) because it operates to hide the possessor. There are many well-known examples, such as the small cabbage white caterpillar, the green flies on roses and the eyed hawk-moth caterpillar on an apple bough.

(2) WARNING COLORATION. However, a few animals are unpalatable for some reason, for instance because they have a nasty taste or are covered with irritant hairs. Others are capable of defending themselves with poison or by emitting offensive smells. It is to the advantage of such unpalatable or dangerous animals that they should be easily recognised by potential predators, so that once a predator has tried to eat such a form and found it unsuitable, it shall be able to recognise and avoid the same animal the next time it is encountered. The rapid recognition of unpalatable or dangerous forms is facilitated either by vivid patterns, smell (skunk), or by some easily recognised noises. Such sounds as the rattle of a rattle-snake, the hiss of a cat or snake, the growl of a threatened dog, all serve to warn intruders that these animals are dangerous, and if molested, will be able to put up a good fight. Normally an intruder, presumably as a result of similar encounters when it was younger and less wise, takes notice of the warning and avoids the dangerous animal.

In other instances it is a particular colour scheme that

makes an unpleasant animal conspicuous, and such an animal is said to show warning coloration. Ernest Neal, in his book on the badger,[1] says that after watching badgers for some years he is convinced that the bold black and white stripes on the head and snout have a warning function, to prevent attack by other animals (e.g. fox). The badger has a wicked bite and would be well able to look after itself in a fight.

A pattern made of black and yellow is very commonly found on unpalatable or on well-armed insects (e.g. hornets, wasps and bumble bees). Several moth caterpillars are also coloured black and yellow (or orange), a good example being the cinnabar moth (*Hipocrita jacobaea*) so frequently to be found in August feeding on ragwort (*Senecio jacobaea*).

The unpalatability of such forms may be tested by offering them to inexperienced hens, i.e. hens which have been penned all their lives. Normally such fowls will eagerly seize any small live object thrown to them. If the object is unpalatable the hen will in a second or so reject it with obvious disgust. If a second specimen is offered a little later the fowl will probably refuse to peck at it.

A warning against forming hasty conclusions from experiments with fowls must be given here. During the course of experiments with town-bred and reared fowls, I discovered that the fowls would not at first take ordinary earthworms. The explanation seems to be as follows. Young chicks peck indiscriminately at any object that catches their eye, and probably, if allowed free range, rapidly learn to discriminate between palatable and unpalatable food. This experience serves them for the rest of their lives. If you watch a broody hen with chicks you will observe how she draws their attention to edible matter. Chicks reared under intensive conditions, in batteries or with restricted runs, do

[1] Ernest Neal, *The Badger*, Collins New Naturalist Monographs.

not come into contact with a great variety of organisms, and so their experience is limited. That is why they will at first peck at caterpillars showing warning coloration, whereas chicks reared on full range, which have usually learned the significance of warning colour, usually refuse.

It should be mentioned here that certain creatures which show warning coloration are impostors. They are neither unpalatable nor harmful, but are taking advantage of the fact that the black and yellow livery is worn so widely by harmful creatures that most predators usually do not molest its wearers, and so the fraud goes undetected. In addition, it should be noted that unpalatable forms may have other colour schemes instead of black and yellow—the ordinary adult cabbage white butterflies are unpalatable to birds, which, in consequence, make no attempt to molest them. Occasionally a bird may be seen pursuing a white butterfly, but it is likely that this is a young bird that has not yet discovered that these butterflies are not good to eat (see p. 73).

Experiment, by offering different kinds of organisms to fowls or cage-birds, on the relationship between colour and palatability. Bear in mind that what is unpalatable to one kind of bird may not be so to another, and that neither poultry nor cage-birds form part of the indigenous[1] fauna of the British Isles, so that conclusions based on their behaviour may not be valid for the wild fauna.

The writer knew a dog which had a passion for killing and eating wasps. He killed them by snapping with his mouth and was apparently never stung.

Minnow colour change

Most anglers know how very difficult it is to see minnows in a stream if they are motionless. This is true whatever the colour of the bottom may be, and suggests that minnows

[1] Indigenous = native, i.e. not imported from abroad.

have some power of changing their colour to match the particular background on which they happen to be.

This may easily be tested. Two large tins (e.g. 7-lb. jam or marmalade tins) are obtained and the interior of one is painted black. The other should have a shiny metallic surface. Place equal quantities of water in each of the tins so that they are about half-full. The water from the stream or lake the minnows come from is the best, but rain water will do. Tap water is not usually good for small creatures.

Then obtain, by netting or some other method which does not injure the fish, a few minnows—six would be a good number. Place half in one tin and half in the other. Stand the tins outside in a good light, and after some hours compare the colours of the minnows. It will probably be found that those minnows which had been kept in the bright tin are much more silvery than those from the tin painted black.

Anglers who use minnows as live bait frequently keep them in tins or bait cans which have shiny interiors and no lids. The effect of this is to make the minnows turn silvery, when they are much more efficient as bait, presumably because they are more easily seen in the water by the carnivorous fish, perch and pike.

Response of Miller's Thumb to light

The curious little fish, the miller's thumb or bully head (*Cottus gobio*), which is to be found in abundance hiding under stones in streams, is usually so difficult to distinguish against the background of gravel that it suggests it has the ability to change colour. This can be investigated if two or more small dishes about 10 in. × 8 in. × 2 in. in dimensions are available. I use the dishes I use for photography, which happen to be black and white.

Obtain, say, six fish from the stream and place three in

the white dish and three in the dark dish. Add river water to cover them. Leave the white dish in good light, but put a cover (I use a folded newspaper with a book on it as a cover) over the black dish. Put the fish together again after five or six hours and compare. You will find that the fish in the white dish are quite pale—those from the black dish are extremely dark, and their light pattern has disappeared. How long does it take these fishes to regain their original colour?

It would be interesting to see what would be the effect of white paper with $\frac{1}{2}$-in., $\frac{1}{4}$-in., and $\frac{1}{8}$-in. black squares (so that a draughtboard pattern is formed), with fish on top of the patterns in their dishes exposed to daylight. It is best to place the fish in clear glass dishes and stand these dishes on the various draughtboard patterns.

MISCELLANEOUS

Do the whiskers of cats, rabbits and mice continue to grow throughout life?

The whiskers of an adult cat remain at a constant length. If they continue to grow then they must wear out at the tips, otherwise the whiskers would become longer and longer.

With scissors cut off the whiskers of a cat on one side of its face (this causes no more pain than a hair-cut does to us). In about three weeks' time the whiskers on both sides of the cat's face will be the same length. Hence the whiskers *do* grow, at least on the side where they were cut.

It may be argued that this growth is only in response to the cutting: that unmolested whiskers do not grow. This may be disproved in two ways.

(1) Examine the ends of a few whiskers under a lens, and some of them will be seen to be wearing thin in places,

H

and almost breaking.   Some may have the tips broken and
hanging by the slenderest of attachments.

(2) Choose a cat with white whiskers, and make three
or four marks at equally-spaced intervals along a whisker
using waterproof Indian ink.   In the course of a few days
the marks will have moved towards the end of the whisker.
They disappear one by one.   This is a conclusive demonstration that the hairs grow and wear out at their tips.

It is not true that a cat or rabbit uses its whiskers to gauge
the width of holes through which its body can pass.   Usually
the body will pass through holes whose diameters are
considerably less than the span of the whiskers, but the
whiskers do have a sensory function.   The few ' whiskers '
in the two groups on the forehead of a cat, above its eyes,
presumably warn it of objects in front of it in the dark.

Sometimes when there are several tame mice in the same
cage you will find that all the mice except one have very
short whiskers.   The exception has normal whiskers.   Could
you find out whether this mouse is eating the whiskers of the
others, or are they normally very short-whiskered ?

Rooks' nests

If tall trees are observed during a gale, it is obvious that
nests built in them must be firmly fixed into the branches
if they are not to be blown down.   The distance of a nest
from the main trunk clearly is one factor determining how
much the nest will be swayed and lashed about during heavy
winds, and another is the mode of growth of the smaller
branches which will determine how securely the nests can
be fixed by interlacing the finest branches with twigs.

Rooks frequently begin nesting in late January or early
February and it is then possible to make simple line diagrams
to show the positions of the various nests forming a rookery.
If this is done and the rookery is revisited after a gale, it

may be found that some of the nests have disappeared. Only those nests which are firmly interlocked into the branches of the tree will survive. (Fig. 19.)

To find out more concerning which trees are favoured by rooks, collect twigs from the trees in as many rookeries as possible. (The trees can usually be identified from a

March 13   April 16

FIG. 19.—Diagram of rooks' nests being formed in black poplars. A nest present on the 13th March was later removed by stormy winds. More nests were built by 16th April.

flora book such as Prime & Deacock's *How to Identify British Trees and Shrubs*.)

Make a list of the trees containing rookeries, and put in the number of rookeries you have discovered in each kind of tree. It will be obvious, of course, that in any district the availability of a particular tree will be an important factor. In many parts, for instance, beeches are absent. Nevertheless, interesting information can be obtained concerning the nesting habits of rooks in specific areas. Such an investigation would make a suitable group activity for a school class, a scout troup or a local natural history society group, or perhaps you could enlist the help of friends living in different areas.

CHAPTER FIVE

LOWER PLANTS

FUNGI

Spore prints of fungi

Spores of the toadstool-like fungi are produced in great numbers, and in the mass appear to have a definite colour which is not always that of the gills. For instance, fungi whose gills appear to be very dark brown, or black, may produce white spores.

The simplest method to discover the colour of the spores from a particular fungus of mushroom shape is to make a ' spore print '. To do this the fungus must be gathered soon after the cap is fully expanded. The stalk should be cut off close to the cap, and the cap placed with its gills downwards onto a sheet of clean white paper. The fungus and the paper on which it rests should be placed in still air such as is found in a cupboard. Alternatively, if it is left in the open a basin should be inverted over the fungus.

When the fungus cap is lifted after about twelve hours there will usually be found on the paper a pattern of the gills made by spores which have fallen from them. The colour of the spores is at once apparent. If the spores happen to be white in colour, a second spore print made on black or dark brown paper should be made.

It is quite interesting to make a permanent collection of spore prints from various fungi. This may be done by making the original prints on waxed paper such as is used to contain cornflakes. When a suitable print has been obtained the waxed paper should be cautiously warmed—

placing it on an electric hotplate is a good method—until the wax just begins to melt. It should then be quickly removed from the source of heat. The spores will have sunk into the wax and will no longer easily rub off or become smudged. Such waxed prints may conveniently be stored between the leaves of a book.

Dung fungus (*Pilobolus*)

Take some fresh horse dung, about the size of a tennis ball, place it on a saucer and cover it with a jam-pot. After a few days it will be seen to be covered with a fine white felt of fungal threads (*mycelia*) and sometimes, at first, the fruiting bodies of *Mucor*, spherical black heads on stalks about ½ in. to 1 in. long. This fungus we do not want, but it will be followed soon by the common Phycomycete fungus *Pilobolus* (Fig. 20). The fungus is easily recognised under a hand lens because of the char-

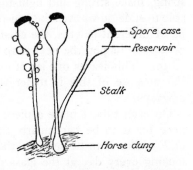

Spore case
Reservoir
Stalk
Horse dung

FIG. 20.—*Pilobolus* sporangiophores formed on horse manure. The liquid globules always present are shown only on the left-hand specimen.

acteristic shape of the sporangiophore which at its tip bears a sporangium—at first white but finally intense black. There are several species, and I may say here that I have never had fresh horse manure which failed to yield a crop of *Pilobolus*.

When the spores are ripe the sporangium containing them is forcibly projected from the end of the sporangiophore and it travels a surprising distance into the air. The sporangiophores when ripe point directly towards the source of strongest light, i.e. they are positively phototropic. In addition, crops of sporangia are shot off at certain times only. The sporangia are sticky and adhere to glass. These facts may be verified as follows:

(1) *To what distance are the sporangia fired?*

Place some fresh horse dung in five jam-pots, so that it comes about half-way up in each. Using appropriate rectangles of newspaper and either sticky tape or pieces of string, make strong and light-tight cylinders which will be able to slide down over the jam-pots. The cylinders should be of different lengths, the smallest ending 6 in. above the manure in its pot, the next at 10 in., then 14 in., and finally 18 in. This leaves one jar of manure without a cover, and the purpose of this is to let you see when the *Pilobolus* develops.

On each tube I place a piece of clean glass (there is no need for it to be particularly tight-fitting). When plenty of *Pilobolus* is to be seen in the jar without a cover, start looking every day at the glass plates on the others. You will soon find crowds of jet-black sporangia sticking to the glass, certainly on the lower two. I will not tell you about the 14 in. and 18 in. because the first time I carried out this experiment my longest tube was 12 in. from the dung, and the glass of this was certainly plastered with black sporangia, as seen through a hand lens. I do know now how far these very tiny packets of spores are fired: I know also that you will enjoy finding out the distance for yourself.

(2) *Are the sporangia projected towards the light?*

In the previous experiment it is quite possible that the *Pilobolus* spores were fired in all directions, and not particularly directed at the glass cover. This can easily be tested.

Take two cocoa tins and put into each two pieces of fresh horse dung. Across the mouth of the first tin lay a suitable sheet of glass, and with Indian ink mark on it the outline of the tin's rim. On the mouth of the second tin place a similar piece of glass, marked in its centre with a circle the size of a halfpenny. Over this place a piece of opaque card (or black paper as used to wrap photographic paper) in which you have cut a hole to coincide with the small circle on the glass. The card or paper must completely cover the mouth of the tin and the hole in it must lie directly above the small circle on the glass. Put an extra sheet of glass on both tins, on the second to hold down the card and on the first so that it (the control) is the same as the other. Leave the two tins in a good light for ten days or so (the growth of the *Pilobolus* depends on the temperature). Then examine the lower glass sheets and draw your conclusions from the distribution of sporangia sticking to the glass. The sporangia are quite visible to the naked eye. I have used horse dung obtained in January from a stable, but have found very much better crops of *Pilobolus* grow upon horse dung collected from grazing fields later in the year. Can you think why this is likely? (If not, consult the pages on *Pilobolus* in *Structural Botany—Flowerless Plants*, written by the late D. H. Scott and extensively revised in 1955 by Prof. Ingold. It is published by Black.)

(3) *What is the fluid which exudes from the sporangiophore?*

The stalk which has the sporangium on the end has many quite large droplets of fluid—which looks like water—along its length as it ripens. They are the result of pressure inside the stalk, pressure which causes some of the fluid the stalk has accumulated to pass to the outside through the wall. The droplets are easy to see with a hand lens.

Test whether these droplets contain water by obtaining

some anhydrous copper sulphate on a dry fine paint brush, and applying it (under a hand lens) to see if it turns blue.

Try to obtain some of the droplets on a sheet of very clean thin glass. When the fluid evaporates does it leave anything which it had dissolved in it ?

(4) *Are other fungi present in horse manure?*

Leave fresh horse manure in an open jam-pot. At first it sweats owing to bacteria. Then after one or two weeks the *Mucor* and afterwards the *Pilobolus* appear—the time depends on the temperature—and by the time the *Pilobolus* has died down the manure is becoming quite dry.

Keep it in the pot and place a sheet of glass across the top. Cover the rest of the jar with black paper to exclude light.

Do you obtain any other spores?

Retain the horse manure for six months and see if you get any small fungi of the mushroom type. It may be well worth while to split open the manure after two or three months.

An anti-aircraft gun (Sphaerobolus fungus)

There is a tiny fungus, no more than two millimetres across, which one may find from time to time growing upon rotting wood. Frequently a weft of greyish fungal hyphae connects the various fruiting bodies. These are white or yellowish, and consist of a double-walled cup, the walls connected only at the rim.

The outer wall splits in a star-shaped pattern, revealing a single sticky mass of spores (called the peridiolum). The inner wall of the cup suddenly turns inside out, throwing the spore mass a considerable distance into the air. It is claimed that it can go almost twenty feet. My first experience of *Sphaerobolus* was obtained by unwittingly bending over a group of these fungi whilst searching for beetles on an old tree stump. Suddenly I received a sharp sting on my cheek and, a few seconds after, another on the brow. Looking down I saw these tiny stars of *Sphaerobolus*. I have never tried to substitute lead shot for the spore mass, but it is said to be an easy task, and then if the fungus is placed under a bell-jar the lead shot will ping with considerable force on the glass of the bell-jar dome.

The Honey Cap Agaric (*Armillaria mellea*)

It is not at all uncommon, when one is walking through woodland, to come across clusters of fungi at the foot of a tree trunk. The fungi in such a cluster vary in size, some being as much as five inches across the cap, others much smaller. The caps are dark reddish-brown (ochraceous) in the centre and usually change towards the edge to a honey colour (that is normal honey, of course; actually honey varies enormously in colour from definite red to pale green). There is a ring on the stem of each toadstool, and when ripe the caps turn up slightly to show the gills which run a little way down the stem. The fungus is called the Honey Cap Agaric, and is a parasite on trees, doing a great deal of damage. The tree finally dies.

The fungus spreads from tree to tree by means of black flattened strands of hyphae, the bigger ones of which resemble black shoe laces in size and shape. These rhizomorphs are worth searching for under the bark of dead trees in the neighbourhood. They lie between the bark and the wood and may be so dense that they form a kind of small meshed net.

Insect parasites on fungi

If you break open the caps of old mushrooms you will find in them a number of tunnels, and most likely also a number of maggots. This is true of very many fungi, and it is an intriguing task to hatch the adults from the maggots. I have done so on a number of occasions, simply by putting the fungal cap into a jam-pot, placing a cap on the pot and awaiting events. If the fungus seems at all wet, let it rest on a layer of newspaper balls the size of walnuts. The large tree fungus, dryad's saddle (*Polyporus squamosus*), projecting as a shelf from elm and other tree trunks, dries very well and it is usually quite rewarding to place several pieces in a covered jam-pot. You should obtain two-winged flies, beetles, and, very likely, small moths. One of the beetles is black with red spots, and I identified it as *Dacne*. Does this dryad's saddle fungus possess gills ?

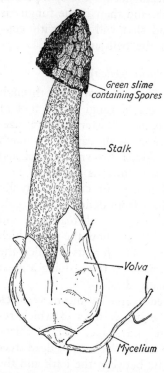

Green slime containing Spores

Stalk

Volva

Mycelium

FIG. 21.—A common stinkhorn, still covered with some of the substance containing spores.

Stinkhorns

The specimens (Fig. 21) one usually obtains of the common stinkhorn (*Ithyphallus impudicus*) are white, but when they first burst out from the large egg-like bodies under the soil the caps are covered with a dark olive-green substance which is sweet to the taste. It is extraordinary how quickly this substance, which contains the spores, is cleared by insects. In a larch wood I watched a stinkhorn which was still covered in the viscid material, and there were several large two-winged flies on it. There were also four brachelytra beetles, i.e. the kind that have short wing cases and so show several abdominal segments. These beetles were very actively moving over the stinkhorn cap, but when touched they fell at once to the ground and could not be found among the detritus on the floor.

It would be interesting to spend several hours watching a newly-emerged stalk and cap, and to make a list of the various types of insects visiting it. The fungal spores in the gluten on the cap are of course spread by the insects. Many people have written that the stinkhorn has a foul smell. To me, the smell is not in the least offensive. What do you think ?

Fern Prothalli

The spores produced on the under-surface of fern leaves give rise to small heart-shaped plants growing flattened against the soil. These are the fern prothalli, a quite distinct generation of plants from the ferns themselves. The ferns give rise to spores from which grow prothalli. The prothalli then produce eggs and spermatozoa which, after fertilisation, give rise to the next generation of ferns.

Fern prothalli are small delicate plants, and cannot live in dry situations. In most parts of England they are not easy to find. Bracken spreads by underground stems, but near bracken one may sometimes come across bracken prothalli in the entrance to a rabbit burrow, where the atmosphere is moister than it usually is outside. Other fern prothalli may be found in wet places among rocks, or in the wet cracks in walls built to restrain land. I used to find prothalli every year on one such wall in the centre of Coventry.

Fern prothalli can sometimes be grown inside a glass jar with a well-fitting stopper. I found a 1-lb. squat honey-jar served well.

Take a piece of broken plant-pot, approximately 2 in. × 2 in., and after boiling and cooling it, sprinkle it *thinly* on one side with fern spores, obtained in October from the sporangia underneath a fern leaf (or along the edges in bracken). Place this piece of plant-pot, with the spores uppermost, on the bottom of the honey-jar, add sufficient water to keep

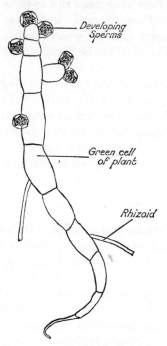

FIG. 22.—A dwarf fern pro-thallus, which is producing only male reproductive cells.

FIG. 23.—A bottle with its neck end broken off is partly sunk into the ground. Fern prothalli will some-times grow inside such bottles.

the plant-pot damp throughout, replace the lid of the jar and stand the jar in a reasonably well-lighted place (but not in direct sunlight).

After some weeks the spores will germinate and cover the plant-pot with green growth. If the spores have not been too thickly sown some may develop into prothalli by the next late spring. If they are too thickly spread it is likely that the spores will develop into much-reduced prothalli bearing only male organs (Fig. 22).

It is said that if a bottle has its neck knocked off so as to leave a jagged edge, and is then pushed, open end first, into the ground in a slanting manner so as to enclose a quantity of soil but leaving an air space above (Fig. 23), then fern prothalli often appear on the surface of this soil. Whether fern prothalli do grow under such conditions probably depends on the water-retaining power of the soil and on whether fern spores are actually present in the soil. I have never tried this. Fern prothalli grow quite easily on sterilised soil, if it is kept moist. A good way to obtain spores is, in autumn, to inspect the under-surface of fern leaves until you see some sporangia have burst. Then remove a piece of the leaf and place it in a paper bag. Tie this bag and put it in a dry place for a fortnight. There should be plenty of spores present in the general debris when you empty the bag onto a sheet of paper.

CHAPTER SIX

HIGHER PLANTS

How do duckweeds pass the winter?

In many of our British ditches, ponds, canals and other stretches of slow-moving water it is possible to find floating near the margins some of those curious plants called duckweeds. They are peculiar in that there are no leaves, the

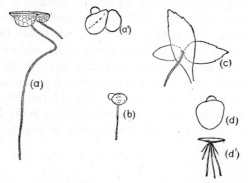

FIG. 24.—Duckweeds: (*a*) Gibbous Duckweed, from the side; (*a'*) the same from above; (*b*) Lesser Duckweed, seen obliquely from above; (*c*) Ivy-leaved Duckweed, from below; (*d*) and (*d'*) Greater Duckweed, from above and from the side. (All × 1½.)

plant consisting of a flattened stem (a thallus it is called) from which one or more adventitious roots are given off. There are four species of duckweed (Fig. 24) and they sometimes (though rarely) produce very tiny flowers in a pocket at the edge of the thallus. It is a stimulating thing to examine them for flowers during July, but you are likely to be successful only with the common duckweed (*Lemna minor*) growing in shallow ditches or even on land where the water level has fallen.

The ordinary duckweed is by far the commonest, as well as being also the smallest (1·5 to 4 mm. across). There is a single root hanging down from the thallus. The gibbous duckweed (*L. gibba*) looked at from above is very similar to the common duckweed, though it is slightly larger (3 to 5 mm. across). However, it may easily be identified by the swollen lower surface which is half-spherical in shape. Both the common and the gibbous duckweeds sometimes occur in vast numbers, completely covering the surface of a pond or parts of a slow river.

The great duckweed (*L. polyrrhiza*) has a flat shiny stem more or less circular in outline, and the underneath surface is often purplish. Each plant gives off several roots from about the centre of the thallus under-surface. In the late summer these great duckweeds are said to bud off kidney-shaped winter buds which at first float on the surface but in a cold winter sink to the bottom of the water. There they remain until the following spring, when they rise to the surface once more and develop into mature plants. Investigate this hibernation by collecting a dozen plants in late August or early September, and placing them in a tin which contains some mud and water from the habitat where you obtained the greater duckweed. Towards Christmas, place the tin in soil up to its brim, so that frost may act on the buds. Do they sink ? If they do, watch for them to float to the surface in the spring.

The ivy duckweed (*L. trisulca*) normally floats just below the surface, and has the shape shown in Fig. 24 (*c*).

In autumn obtain a dozen of each of the common, gibbous and ivy duckweeds and set up for each species a tin sunk into the garden up to the brim. Put in each about 1 in. of mud from where you obtained the duckweed, and fill the tins with water from the same place or places. Examine the plants each month from November until the end of April.

It is often said that duckweeds (except the great duckweed which dies) sink to the bottom to pass the winter, and that one of them roots in the soil. Do they all sink ? With a pair of forceps you could soon find out if a sunken plant were rooted to the bottom.

Arum maculatum

The leaves of the wild arum (*Arum maculatum*) can be found in hedgerows from March until June. Some have purplish-black patches on the leaves; others are quite free from markings. Are all the leaves of a particular plant spotted, or are they entirely free from spots ? Or are some leaves spotted and others of the same plant not spotted ? Are there other constant differences, such as in size or texture, to justify the regarding of plants with spotted leaves as a distinct variety ?

Can you discover *Arum* leaves that appear to have been partially eaten ?

Cautiously nibble *a little* of an *Arum* leaf, keeping the leaf at the front of the mouth, until a severe burning sensation is felt at the tip of the tongue. Then spit out the chewed leaf at once because it contains needle-shaped crystals of calcium oxalate. This experiment demonstrates one kind of plant defence mechanism against predatory animals such as slugs and caterpillars.

If a thin transverse section is cut from the leaf and it is viewed under the high-power lens of a microscope, tiny spicules will be visible. It is these spicules, penetrating the lips and tongue, that give rise to the burning sensation. In olden times *Arum* leaves were fed to slaves who had escaped and been recaptured.

PLATE V

A—On the end leaf of the twig of hawthorn is a clutch of lacewing fly eggs. Aphids can be seen covering the inner leaf stalks.

B—Hoary plantains growing in February.

PLATE VI

The inset shows a complete arum inflorescence, with one leaf. The main part of the photograph shows the lower part of a young arum inflorescence, the outer wall of which has been removed. The female flowers are at the bottom, followed by a ring of sterile ovaries. Above is the belt of male flowers (not yet ripe) and finally some sterile stamens at present forming a one-way valve—flies can get inside the spathe (outside wall) but cannot yet normally escape. A few flies are still present here. The dark structure is the base of the dark red spadix.

Is the curious deep crimson spadix of importance in attracting the small insects (chiefly gall midges) that pollinate this flower?

At about the middle of April find a hedgerow in which *Arum* is abundant, and carefully remove the spadixes from several inflorescences which are almost, but not quite, open. Leave an approximately equal number of ' flowers ' untreated. Mark with sticks, or in some other way, the treated ' flowers '. This is important, as the vegetation of hedge banks is growing extremely quickly at this time, and after a few days the plants operated upon may be difficult to find. In three or four days examine some of the control plants which have since opened. If they are found to contain midges when the wall of the bulbous swelling forming the base of the spathe is cut away with a knife, open the bases of the treated arums (Plate VI). Are any midges or other insects present in them? Do your results throw any light on the significance of the spadixes?

Ovules on female yew

Everyone must be familiar with the bright red arils which appear on female yew at the end of the summer, but it is surprising how few people know where and when to look for the ovules which give rise to the red arils. The ovules ripen at the same time as the stamens of the male cones, organs which bedeck the branches of the male trees with a light golden colour at the end of February and during March, and which give off great clouds of pollen if shaken on a still day. Look, on such a day, underneath the tips of the branches of female trees, but use a hand lens if you possibly can. Snug against the leaf-covered twigs you will find ovules in ones and twos, which may at first appear to be buds, but which can be identified by the hole at the free end where the nucellus has opened. There will very likely

I

be mucilage on the walls of the nucellar channel, but it is not likely that you will see it. However, on some of the ovules there will be globules as big as themselves, projecting out to catch pollen (Plate III, c). Gradually the globules evaporate and the pollen is withdrawn into the nucellus and there it germinates.

Take a few twigs from a female tree and place their broken stalks in a vase of water. Examine the specimens you have from time to time, and with a hand lens you will be certain to find globules on some of the ovules.

It is worth while, during the pollination period, to test an observation of the natural historian, Kerner. He wrote more than half a century ago:

'. . . one may see the female plants, on a sunny morning sparkling in the sunshine as it were with dew drops. These " dew drops " are in reality droplets of mucilage, excreted from the micropyles of the ovules, awaiting the chance deposition by the wind of pollen grains.'

Hoary plantains

The hoary plantains (*Plantago media*) occur on many lawns and parks, but certainly not on all. They are worth looking at towards the end of February and beginning of March (Plate V, B). Then each hoary plantain will have only a small rosette of leaves, the bigger leaves having rotted away. However, the spaces left remain free of intruding vegetation, and the hoary plantains fill the spaces again when their leaves renew growth.

I have wondered (a) whether dead hoary plantain leaves contain poison ? (b) Whether the way the plantain leaves lie very flat and press tightly to the ground excludes seeds from falling there ? Are there any seeds ?

Perhaps you could do experiments if you know where

these plantains grow. For instance, in March dig out a thin ($\frac{1}{2}$ in.) layer of the bare soil from around these plantains and fill a 3-in. plant-pot. Fill another with ordinary garden soil. Now spread twenty soaked mustard seeds on the surface of the soil in each pot. They will germinate, if they are going to do so, long before the wild plant seeds which may be present. The result will show you if there is any poison which has passed from the rotting plantain leaves into the soil. I do not say there will or will not be poison.

Alternatively, try the effect of sowing a few mustard seeds in (a) the bare region of a hoary plantain, and (b) in a comparable bare place in the main garden. Protect each place against birds by making a covering network of black cotton, or use small-mesh wire netting. As spring comes nearer, you may have to remove the new season's growth of plantain leaves.

To find out if there are any seeds under a plantain, fill a 3-in. plant-pot with soil from around the plantain. If you have discovered the presence of poison then pour six half-pint jugfuls of rain water through the pot. Those should remove any poison present. Now set aside the plant-pot on a saucer, and cover it with a sheet of glass. Keep the soil moist (but not wet) and see if any seeds germinate in, say, six months.

FERTILITY OF WILD PLANTS

Germinating wild plants

It is worth while to make some little investigation into the germination of wild plants in which you are interested. Suppose you choose four or five plants such as knapweed, hogweed, groundsel, dandelion and yarrow. Others plants, of course, may suit you better—it does not matter.

Obtain one or more seed-boxes (or plant-pots) and nearly fill the box with good seedling mixture which you may make from humus, soil and sand.   One part of each would do. Alternatively, obtain good loam from the garden and mix silver sand with it, one part of silver sand to two of loam. Sterilise the seed mixture by a thorough heating in the oven at about 120° C.—up to three or four hours—and then make the mixture thoroughly wet.   If you are using a seed-box to investigate the germination of your chosen plants, divide it into five areas using thin wooden partitions.   Also obtain a sheet of glass to cover it.

When the soil has drained off its water, then plant 25, or 50, or, even better, 100 seeds in each area, using only one kind of plant seed in each area, of course.   Cover the seeds with a light layer of soil, put the sheet of glass over and place the box in the greenhouse or in a sheltered spot in the garden.   Then wait for germination results.   It is best to do this experiment in spring, but remember that some seeds take a long time to germinate (e.g. hawthorn), so do not be too impatient.   Also, you must keep the soil moist.

Obtaining seeds

The seeds of many plants may be obtained in quantity by enclosing the ripening inflorescence in a polythene (or wax-paper) bag, tying the mouth of the bag firmly to the stem.   When the fruit of similar plants nearby are ripe, cut off the inflorescence stem a little way below the bag mouth and hang it in an airy place for a few more days. There should be plenty of seeds.   In the case of certain low plants, such as pearlwort, the above procedure is not possible.   In such cases you will have to nip off nearly ripe fruit heads and put them into paper bags, again leaving them for several days to ripen off.

You will have noticed that all the ' seeds ' I mentioned

in the opening paragraph are really fruits or parts of dry fruits containing a single seed. It would be interesting to obtain some of these 'seeds' from dandelion and groundsel in the very late autumn, or even in January and February (from groundsel). These late-produced fruits often look withered and empty. Can they germinate?

You will find plenty of interesting things relating to other plants. For instance, dog's mercury flowers are mostly male, but a few are female and produce dry fruit. However, if you try to germinate the seeds you will find the number germinating is as low as 5 per cent. Plantains, on the other hand, will, if sown in September or October, quite soon germinate, but usually not all of them. Then, after February, most of the remaining ones will germinate.

FIG. 25.—A method of growing seeds in a plant-pot resting in a 2-lb. jam-pot. A cotton wool strand carries moisture from the water in the jam-pot to the soil in the plant-pot.

Growing seeds in small pots

Growing seeds in many small pots can make rather a big job. I solved the problem by obtaining some cotton wool and some 2-lb. jam-jars into which the pots fitted. Then, when filling the pots with the germination soil, I included a thin rope of cotton wool which came out at the bottom hole of the plant-pot. This cotton wool carried water which I placed in the jam-pot at such a level that it was about 1 in. below the bottom of the pot, which thus was not flooded with water. However, by capillary attraction of the cotton wool, water was delivered to the soil, which remained beautifully moist at the surface. More water was added as necessary (Fig. 25). Incidentally, a small pot of soil may be effectively sterilised by placing the pot on a saucer and pouring about two pints of boiling water through it. After twenty minutes the seeds may be planted.

An experiment with chickweed

Try this experiment with chickweed. Take several sheets of blotting paper and cut them to the size of a jam-jar mouth. Place them on a saucer, put twenty-four chickweed (*Stellaria media*) seeds on the blotting paper, add water and cover with a jam-jar. Keep the blotting paper moist. Very likely the seeds will not germinate, even after two or three months. Then pick up the twelve seeds from one half of the blotting paper and give them one or two scratches with a needle. Replace these with the others, making a mark to identify their position, and see what happens. The results may enable you to explain why so many chickweed seedlings appear after you have dug the garden.

Some factors which may affect seed germination

The three experiments which follow are concerned with conditions in the soil rather than with the traditional experiments carried out in laboratories, where the seeds are required to germinate out of their true environment. Of course, there are other factors besides the ones mentioned below.

(1) Does unsterilised soil affect the percentage germination of seeds?

I have insisted already that in experiments with seeds you must use sterilised soil. What happens if you do not—if you merely take some garden soil and sow seeds in that?

May I suggest that you use polyanthus seeds ? I say this because when I was a boy of ten or eleven years old it was a row of polyanthus plants that first gave me, as a result of a little experiment, the knowledge that flowers produce seeds and the seeds will grow into new plants. Up till then I had always believed that seeds came from packets, and I had no idea of how they got into the packets.

I was playing in late summer in a garden which had a long row of polyanthus plants, and around each plant were some quite obvious baby polyanthuses. I wondered how they got there, and I discovered the open fruit capsules fringed with their row of teeth. Some of them rattled when shaken and I was able to break them off and shake what appeared to be seeds from them, though I could not be sure they were seeds.

With some eagerness I shook out as many of these particles as I could find, sealed them in an envelope cadged from the owner of the garden, and went happily home. I carried out the obvious experiment of planting these particles in our garden, just as we planted radish and lettuce seed from packets.

I waited impatiently—I knew it took seeds a little time to ' come up '—but eventually baby polyanthus plants appeared where I had sown the seeds and so proved that my guess (hypothesis) was correct. It was this experiment which gave me, as a boy, an interest in plants and later in botany as a whole.

What I suggest you do is merely to sow a definite number of polyanthus seeds (collected from plants in July), say 100, in sterilised garden soil and the same number in another pot, this time of unsterilised soil. Find after some months the percentage germination of each batch. Does the sterilisation of the soil make any difference, i.e. did your results incline you to think that one or other of the soils was hampering germination ?   I must warn you that statisticians who understand the Laws of Probability might say that any difference in germination numbers between the two soils was not ' significant ', i.e. that they proved nothing because the difference was not great enough.   Mathematical analysis is being used more and more in a wide variety of biological experiments, and biological research workers often have to submit their results to mathematicians before they can reach valid conclusions.   Some biologists are also able mathematicians, for example, Professor J. B. S. Haldane.

Try the experiment with lettuce, snapdragon or any other small seeds that appeal to you.   Do not forget that although most of the seeds of one kind may germinate together, possibly there will be a few ' hard ' seeds which may not germinate until long after the main batch (see plantain, p. 125).   You will realise that this is one reason why, in an experiment of this nature, you should *use as many seeds as possible*, for then you are likely to get almost equal numbers of hard seeds in both soils, and that will help to make your results ' significant '.   If you had only four seeds to use, and two of them were hard seeds, the other two being normal, you might sow the two hard seeds on your sterilised soil and the other two on your unsterilised soil, and this would give you the quite false conclusion that sterilised soil will not allow any of that particular kind of seed to germinate.

(2) *Do ordinary garden seeds germinate in waterlogged soil?*

Obtain a bowl which you can fill with water and in which you can stand three small plant-pots.   Fill the pots with garden soil, sterilise with boiling water and then plant several kinds of seeds—for instance, peas in one pot, mustard in the second and cabbage in the third.   Pine seeds planted in soil from a pine wood are quite interesting.   Count and record the number of seeds planted.   Finally, place the pots in the bowl and add water until its surface is just below the level of the soil in the pots. The soil will rapidly become waterlogged, and you will be able to see how many seeds germinate. You should, of course, have control pots with the various seeds planted in them also. Keep these pots moist and the seeds there should germinate and tell you how long it normally takes at the temperature where the plant-pots are kept. What explanation of your results can you offer ? I can think of two reasons.

(3) *Do seeds germinate in air-dry soil?*

Normally, air-dry soil contains from about 7 per cent to 14 per cent of water. It can be made by taking soil from the garden, sterilising it by one of the methods I have mentioned (p. 126) and then making it into a thin layer ($\frac{1}{4}$ in. to $\frac{1}{2}$ in. thick) on tin trays or even on newspaper, preferably on an outside shed floor. Leave the soil for four or five days, stirring it from time to time. Its water content should by then be in equilibrium with the water vapour in the air.

Now fill two plant-pots with the soil and set them on saucers. Finally, sow in the soil mustard, or some other quickly-germinating seed.

In three weeks have your seeds germinated at all ? If they have not, the experiment does NOT yet tell you that they have not germinated because of the air-dry soil; it may be that the packet contained old seeds which had lost the power to germinate; or the soil may have contained a lethal contaminant (such as, for instance, creosote). To finish the experiment you must add water to the soil in one pot, and keep it moist. The addition of water is best done by standing the pot in water nearly up to the level of the soil. When the surface of the soil is wet, then remove the pot, let it drain, and stand it on a saucer. This is really a CONTROL pot, for if the mustard germinates in it, and there is still no germination in the other pot, then you are justified in saying that ' Air-dry soil does not allow mustard to germinate in it '. The experiment does not answer the question ' Can lettuce (or other seeds) germinate in air-dry soil ? ' Each would have to be tested independently. In fact, of course, gardeners know that seeds planted in a spell of hot weather frequently do not germinate until after a shower of rain.

WEEDS

Weeds on lawns

Certain plants, by their habit and ability, are able to grow upon lawns which are regularly mown, and even to flower and produce seeds. They are worth inspection from time to time, and you will see that there are several methods of survival which may be used. The dandelion in a well-mown lawn lies almost flat in its rosette, but puts up the flower stalks quite persistently. In spring the flower stalks are tall and get cut off by the mower. Gradually the stalks become shorter and shorter until the flower bud is perhaps half an inch or less from the grass, and can pass under the mowing machine. In a short time the bud produces a flower head and with luck may be able to form fruit.

Cut across the root of a dandelion in the lawn, and remove the aerial part of the plant. It now looks as if the dandelion is killed. But wait. In about a fortnight or so you will find that where there was one rosette of leaves there are now several, and a bad weed is now a worse one. Dig it up to see how these smaller dandelions arise.

The particular weeds one finds on a lawn vary to some extent with the area, and also with the care with which the lawn is tended. There are usually some broad-leaved plantains but fewer ribworts. The former can be trodden on repeatedly and not be destroyed easily, but the ribwort tends to grow in grass which is seldom cut, or grassland not frequently trodden over. You may see in a field grazed by milch cows that when you get near the gateway a lot of broad-leaved plantains occur, but very few, if any, ribworts, though these latter will grow freely out in the open pasture. The cows tend to gather round the gate at milking time, and even if they do not, the concentration of footprints as the cows converge on the gate to go to the farm is inevitably higher than in the open field. Similarly, on some footpaths you may find broad-leaved plantains, whilst ribworts flourish in the grass verges.

The manner in which white clover (*Trifolium repens*) and creeping buttercup (*Ranunculus repens*) and some other plants spread over a lawn surface by stems which creep in between the grass plants, is interesting. If one examines such plants there will usually be seen adventitious roots at the nodes on these stems. Flowers of these plants, and of some others, are usually present, hidden between the grass stalks. They are much smaller than when growing in a hedgerow or on waste ground, and they usually look rather starved, though some of the tiny plants such as pearlwort, or mosses, when present usually grow well.

Another group of lawn weeds, of which yarrow (*Achillea millefolium*) and self-heal (*Prunella vulgaris*) are typical examples, reproduce vegetatively by means of underground stems (stolons) which grow through the ground and give rise to new aerial shoots. Yet a third group merely straggle across the ground in between the grass stems, and do not root at the nodes. Common pearlwort (*Sagina procumbens*) is one such, although the procumbent stems which lie among the grass stems do root at the basal nodes. The terminal shoots are more or less vertical.

Pearlwort is probably one of the most widespread lawn weeds. I well remember seeing on a playing field in Warwickshire a largish area covered with what I thought to be moss. I knelt down to examine it and found tiny flowers with very small white petals which told me that I was wrong. This was the first time I became conscious of pearlwort as a lawn weed, but once I had seen it I seemed to find it everywhere. You should look for it whenever you have access to a lawn with which you are not familiar.

Eradication of weeds from lawns

There are several ways in which constantly mown grass-land, such as lawns, tennis courts, putting greens, cricket pitches and bowling greens, may be treated to get rid of weeds, but I am no expert and shall not describe them. There are, however, a few demonstrations you can set up if you have a small piece of weedy lawn available.

Daisies or self-heal can easily be eradicated with ammonium sulphate. Select a square yard of lawn in the middle of a daisy-infested patch and try the effect of treating it with a mixture made of 4 oz. ammonium sulphate and 20 oz. of sand. This should be applied in four lots of 6 oz. each during the growing season, say from the beginning of April until the end of May. Then compare the daisy population in your square with that of the surrounding lawn.

You will know that the growth of plants is to a large extent dependent on the presence of certain chemicals called 'auxins' secreted both at the shoot tip and the root tip. The auxin from the shoot tip passes backwards to the growing region and speeds growth, whilst that from the root tip retards growth.

There are now on the market substances which are closely akin to these growths auxins, and if they are applied by a spray or watering-can (in the dilution advocated by the manufacturers) they produce a remarkable effect. The one I have used is called ' Dicotox ' and I think the name has been coined from the two words *dicotyledon* and *toxin* (poison). It certainly works drastically on the dicotyledons present, making them grow into gross caricatures of the original plants. After a few weeks they die. In a demonstration I did on a Derbyshire lawn three years later the treated area was still almost free from weeds. This particular chemical seems hardly to affect monocotyledons, the group to which grasses belong.

Comparison of a grazing field with a lawn

It is a very good exercise to make a simple analysis of the plants in a lawn (excluding grass) and compare this with a similar analysis of a field grazed by cattle. However, before you can do this investigation you will have to be able to recognise the plants, often when they are small and injured, and frequently when they are not in flower. You can do this only by paying close attention to the common weeds of your area for several years, unless there is someone who is familiar with the local flora to whom you can appeal.

A simple way to do the analyses is to concentrate not on the actual *numbers* of each plant, but on the number of *places* in which the plants grow. To do this you will require a ring of thick wire, about 1 ft. in diameter. A little distortion from a true circle is not important. Now throw the ring in a random fashion and when it has settled note the name of every plant that occurs inside its periphery. The record should be kept on a sheet ruled out first for a vertical list of plant names, and followed by about fifty columns in which you will put a plus if one specimen (or more) of a plant is present in the ring. The diagram in Fig. 26 shows you what I mean. If the ring falls across a plant, count it as ' in ' if half or more of it is inside the ring.

Name of Plant	Throw number											No. of throws present	%age
	1	2	3	4	5	6		47	48	49	50		
Daisy	✓	✓	✓	✓		✓		✓	✓	✓	✓	48	96
Bulbous Buttercup		✓	✓		✓	✓		✓	✓	✓		40	80
Dandelion	✓	✓		✓					✓			30	60
Broad-Leaved Plantain		✓								✓		28	56
Pearlwort	✓			✓	✓			✓	✓		✓	26	52
Hop Trefoil					✓							1	2
Etc.													

FIG. 26.—How to compose a chart of weeds on a lawn.

Throw the ring again, and once more record on your chart the presence of weeds which are there. Probably there will be some new ones which were not recorded in the first throw results, whilst some of the plants ringed by the first throw may not be in the second. Continue this until you have made fifty throws. These should be made so as to get a random sample of all parts of the lawn.

Add the number of occurrences of each plant to get a total, and double the total if you like to work in percentages. Then plot a histogram similar to that shown in Fig. 27, beginning with the plant which has most occurrences and continuing with the next highest, then the third highest and so on in decreasing number of occurrences until you get to the plant with the least number of occurrences.

Now repeat this in a field that is grazed by cattle, but

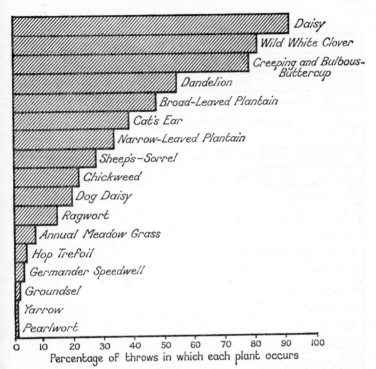

Daisy

Wild White Clover

Creeping and Bulbous-Buttercup

Dandelion

Broad-Leaved Plantain

Cat's Ear

Narrow-Leaved Plantain

Sheep's-Sorrel

Chickweed

Dog Daisy

Ragwort

Annual Meadow Grass

Hop Trefoil

Germander Speedwell

Groundsel

Yarrow

Pearlwort

Percentage of throws in which each plant occurs

FIG. 27.—Histogram of the number of throws which surround each weed with the ring.

when you come to make the histogram put down your plants in the same order as they occur in the lawn histogram, leaving a blank for a lawn species which is not represented in the field. Very likely there will be plants in the field which are not found on the lawn. These should be inserted on the histogram after the last lawn plant (Fig. 28).

If the lawn and field are not too far apart it is not unlikely that the main differences between the flora of them will be due to the regular mowing of the lawn as against the very

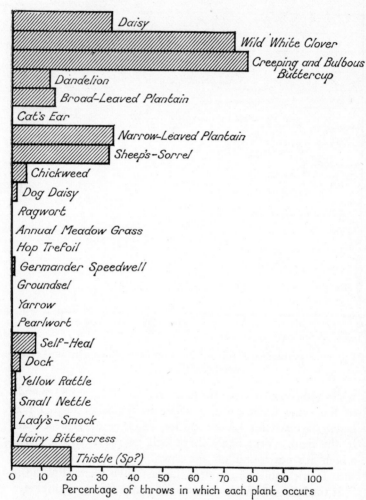

FIG. 28.—Histogram for nearby field grazed by cattle.

PLATE VII

A—Fairy lantern nest, containing eggs of the
spider *Agroeca brunnea*.

B—Pear-leaf sawfly caterpillars, on cherry.

PLATE VIII

A wind-blown hawthorn tree on Exmoor. In the background are wind-blown beeches.

occasional cropping (which is not too close to the ground) by cattle. Sheep, of course, crop very close. The application of different manures to the lawn and the field may also be a factor. Can you find out the manurial record for the last five years ? The differences between the fairway and the rough on a golf course may offer you an opportunity for investigation.

POLLINATION AND SEEDS

Pollination of figwort

The figworts have small flowers which are a dark red in colour. One, *Scrophularia aquatica*, grows commonly along

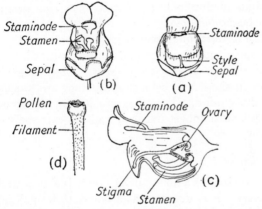

FIG. 29.—Water Figwort (*Scrophularia aquatica*): (*a*) Front view of young flower, in the female stage; (*b*) older flower, in the male stage; (*c*) longitudinal section through a young flower; (*d*) a single stamen to show how the anther liberates the pollen by a terminal transverse slit. (*a*), (*b*) and (*c*), × 3; (*d*), × 6.

river banks and my first insight into its pollination occurred during a fishing contest in which I took part. There was

K

little response from the fish to my bait, and in time my eye began to wander. I heard an occasional buzzing and quite soon I became aware of wasps busy on the figwort flowers, and it was soon apparent they were seeking something in the flower. The ' something ' turned out to be nectar. As far as I can tell, wasps are the only insects which seek this nectar.

The flowers have but four stamens. The dorsal one, the fifth, has in the course of evolution turned into a flat flap of tissue of a nature similar to the petals. This flap is called a staminode, and it has behind it a droplet of nectar. Incidentally, you will soon observe that the youngest flowers protrude the stigma over the lower lip before the stamens are ripe. Such flowers are said to be *protogynous* (Fig. 29). Most kinds of flowers have their stamens ripe first and are said to be *protandrous*.

On the figwort inflorescence in summer, after the flowers have dropped and been replaced by fruit, you will frequently find that *Cionus* beetles are present. They look very like the fruit in shape and colour, and if they are touched they fall to the ground, where they are lost in the grass. The *Cionus* pupate amongst the fruit and are extremely difficult to see.

Pollination of honeysuckle

The structure of a honeysuckle flower is shown in Fig. 30. Quite clearly it is designed as a flower to be pollinated by a long-tongued insect, and you will find that during daylight certain British hawk-moths will hover in front of the flowers and extend their proboscies into the nectar.

However, hawk-moths are only one group, for bumble bees also pollinate it, and very curiously so do hoverflies— a most unexpected group of short-tongued insects. It is well worth while to stay for an hour or so in a wood watching

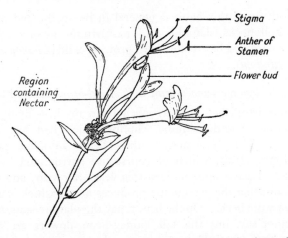

FIG. 30.—Honeysuckle flowers, to show the projecting stigmas and anthers, × ⅔. The honeysuckle is pollinated by hawk-moths and hoverflies.

what does visit honeysuckle. To see a hawk-moth in bright sunlight poised before a honeysuckle flower is an experience one remembers.

Insect-pollinated flowers and the light

Where foxgloves are found growing in shady places, it is rather striking that all the flowers on the spikes (raceme) face towards the direction from which most light comes. This is a mechanical response to uni-directional light, a positive photropism of the flowers, but its adaptive significance is appreciated only when it is remembered that foxgloves are insect-pollinated, the principal pollinating agents being bumble bees. Hive bees do not fly into deep shade, and most kinds of bumble bees fly mainly in the open. Hence a plant growing in shade is more likely to attract the notice of an insect that uses its eyes for discovering plants if all the flowers of that plant are directed towards the open.

Find out if this habit is general in bee-pollinated plants (e.g. hollyhocks, daffodils and nasturtiums among garden plants, and rosebay willow herb growing wild (*Chamaenerion angustifolium*).

Do bees damage runner-bean and broad-bean flowers?

I was astonished one day when I saw my bees flying into white dead nettle clumps, clumps which had lost their flowers. The bees pushed their heads into the young developing fruit, which of course are surrounded by the sepals. I have since noticed this year after year, and have no doubt that the dead nettle produces nectar which is taken away by the bees. Do the bees repay the plant in some way? I cannot say, but the tall kidney-bean flowers are often bitten through the base by bees seeking nectar, and so are broad beans. You will find that the bitten flowers normally fall from the plant in a few days time, and at first sight it seems that the bees are not giving any help to the plant in return for the nectar. Indeed, it seems that the bees are doing harm.

However, you may in fact find, if you look at the *lower* branches of a runner-bean plant (or a broad bean), that all the lower flowers have dropped from the plant. Is this due to the action of bees, or to some internal factor in the plant? To test this tie a number of unopened flower heads into separate bags of cellophane or polythene so that insects cannot have access to the flowers, and merely watch whether the flowers still drop off or now produce beans. Broad beans are self-pollinated and do not require the visits of bees.

Are the runner beans also self-pollinated? You may be able to make an 'informed guess' if you watch the flowers on a warm sunny day and see whether bees enter at least some of the bean flowers. But an informed guess is not enough for a scientist, and you will have to make an experiment to find out the true answer to the question:

Are runner beans self-pollinated ?

Again, you will require a number of polythene bags. These can easily be made from the wrappings of such things as shirts, boxes of chocolate, and very many modern goods and foodstuffs, or they can be bought from a good seed shop.

Select a flower branch with the basal flowers showing the formation of beans whilst the terminal bud is unopened. Snip off all the flowers except the terminal one and enclose this in a bag. Do the same for a number of others. Do these flowers open and in a few days begin to develop a bean ? If so, then they must be self-pollinated. If they do not, then either snipping off the other flowers has affected the end one, or else it requires to be cross-pollinated. To decide between these possibilities it will be necessary to cross-pollinate the flower yourself, and this will need some skill. Enclose a number of end flower buds in separate bags and wait until they are nearly in flower. Then open the flowers carefully and remove the stamens with a needle and pair of forceps. That will leave the style and unripe stigma which must be undamaged. Replace new bags over each dissected flower. When a stigma is ripe untie the bag and with a clean paint-brush transfer to the stigma pollen from the flowers of another plant. Do many of the ovaries develop a bean ? If they fail to do so it may be because you have damaged them, and the result is not conclusive. This objection may be partially overcome by first practising the art of removing the stamens from other runner-bean flowers, which are not to be used for the experiment. Similarly, by observing other bean flowers you should be able to tell when the stigmas are ripe. With a good hand lens you can see pollen adhering to the tips.

Extra-floral nectaries

If you stand by a laurel bush on a warm spring day, you will soon be conscious that flies buzzing about the bush from time to time land on a leaf and disappear under it, to remain for some while. If you turn the leaves so that their undersides are facing upwards, you will see four glands situated along the lower part of the midrib of each. These will look moist, or even wet, and if you care to test them removed from the leaf, you will find the presence of sugar. Which kind of sugar? (see p. 146) Is there any present in the colder seasons?

This is an extra-floral nectary. Such organs are present on a number of plants (e.g. the stipules of the ordinary broad bean have them). It is not easy to see the value to the plant but there they are. The amount of water expelled through them is so small that it can hardly amount to anything useful in the way of pulling water through the plant. It has been suggested that extra-floral nectaries attract ants and so protect the flowers, but even this has a certain lack of probability when one considers a plant such as the laurel.

Parasites in seeds

If you keep your eyes open you will continually come across parasites in seeds. Probably the beetle maggot in developing peas is the best known, but many readers will be familiar with the maggot in hazel nuts. The difficulty with the seeds of wild flowers is that it is extremely hard to identify the insects, though often one can identify beetles found there.

The way to obtain most of these parasites is to place the seeds in a flat-bottomed collecting tube from 2 to 3 ins. long. I put the cork back in and simply leave it until there is agitation amongst the seeds, and there will be a parasite.

Often I find a good number. When searching for parasites on legumes I slip dry pods into the tube and very often the parasites come through the pod wall, eating a round hole. In a number of prostrate broom pods from Dungeness I had a glorious crop of small insects.

Try opening the fruits which finish up as dry fruits. You will probably be surprised how many seeds are eaten away, and if done at the right time, you should find maggots of one kind or another.

Around Bakewell, knapweed (*Centaurea nigra*) is devastated every year by maggots eating the developing fruit in the fruit heads. Does this occur in your area?

What is the difference between a ' light ' and a ' dark ' seed?

Many seeds will germinate either in the light or in darkness. It is known that some seeds show a preference for one or the other, but more rarely for light.

Love-in-a-mist (*Nigella*), or devil-in-a-bush as some prefer, codlins-and-cream (*Epilobium hirsutum*), and cabbage seeds are worth trying. Codlins-and-cream is a tall plant about 4 ft. high, and it grows mainly in dampish soil, so look along river banks, in rough ground near lakes and pools, and in marshy ground. Codlins-and-cream seems to prefer some wind protection either from a nearby coppice or from other plants growing to its own height.

Collect codlins-and-cream seeds when they are ripe. The *Nigella* seeds can be obtained from the garden plant or bought cheaply in a seed shop, as can the cabbage seed.

In the spring obtain a seed-box and fill with good moist soil previously sterilised (see p. 126). Then split it into two halves with a thin piece of board, or cardboard, placed as a vertical partition across the centres of the long sides and as high as the long sides. In one half scatter twenty seeds of each of the three plants, *Nigella*, codlins-and-cream and cabbage, and allow them to lie on top where they fall. Scatter a similar number of the seeds in the other half. Then, finally, obtain a sheet of glass which covers the whole seed-box and mask one compartment of seeds with black paper (or two or three layers of brown paper if there is no black paper). Actually, the side of a cornflake packet glued on to the glass will do very well. The mask should be under the glass, the more effectively to cut off the light.

Allow the seeds to germinate and find out whether each can germinate in both light and dark.

Cress seeds are worth trying, too.

HAWTHORN

Wind-blown hawthorn

On the higher ground, or land exposed to frequent high winds, it is not unusual to find trees whose branches grow very distinctly along one direction only. The other three sides may have tiny—and usually dead—branchlets, which contrast strangely with the apparently strongly-grown branches of the fourth side. Where you see one such tree you will frequently come across many others (see the beech trees in the distance, behind the hawthorn, in Plate VIII). Is the direction of growth the same in all the trees in one area? Do the trees grow away from the direction of the prevailing winds? Are the small twigs pointing towards the windy sides completely dead?

Are haws eaten?

In the hedgerows there are many berries and other fruit ripening in the autumn—wild arum, bryony, rose, hawthorn, crab and so on. It is an easily verified fact that the berries do not all ripen at the same time, neither do the birds eat all these fruits at the same time. Apart from direct observations of birds feeding, much can be discovered about the kinds of fruit being eaten by examining bird droppings. Most succulent fruits have seeds encased in a stony endocarp or a hard testa, and these seeds pass unharmed through the alimentary canals of birds. Indeed, it has been shown that certain seeds (e.g. hawthorn) will germinate readily only after they have been acted upon by the digestive juices of animals.

Collect bird droppings—it will usually be found that certain places are more favoured as perching places than are others—from September until the following March, and examine them for the stones of wild fruit, month by month. A spoon is a useful tool for the actual collection. One needs to collect examples of the various succulent fruit to be found in the area, in order to become familiar with the stones. A useful thing is to mount several examples of the stones of the various fruit upon a postcard, labelling the species at the time of mounting. The wild fruit are easy enough to recognise, but those of the fruiting bushes of gardens not nearly so easy. Parks may give some help.

A search in winter along the bases of hedgerows bearing hawthorns will usually reveal hawthorn stones gnawed by mice, and others that have been split longitudinally by hawfinches. In some areas the freshly split halves of haw-thorn stones are a familiar sight in February and March, even though the hawfinches are not themselves conspicuous.

Haws remain uneaten on the trees usually until well on in January or early February. About this time they become rather squashy to the touch, the flesh now having a meaty consistency whereas previously it was hard. Is this change due, as in so many other fruit, to the conversion of starch into sugar ?

Obtain haws in December and test them with iodine for starch, and with Fehling's solution for reducing and

K*

non-reducing sugar.[1]   Repeat the tests towards the middle
of February, or earlier if they are becoming scarce.

March and April on the farm are hungry months. ' Find
out if there are any berries available for birds at these times.

PLANTS WHICH CLIMB BY TWINING

You will be familiar with many kinds of plants which
climb on other plants; some by hooks or thorns; others by
tendrils; ivy by means of adventitious roots; and some

---

[1] Iodine causes a raw slice of material to turn blue-black if
starch is contained in the material.   Fehling's solution is bought
as Fehling's A and Fehling's B and is stored as such.   When
making a test for reducing sugar mix equal parts of the two solutions,
shake, and introduce to the test-tube the material to be tested.
Heat, preferably over a small gas flame.   The presence of reducing sugar is denoted by a bright red or orange precipitate
of cuprous oxide.   (You can do this test at home using the flame
of a gas stove.)

If there is no reducing sugar it is usual to test for non-reducing
sugar.   To do this some of the material is boiled in a drop or two
of dilute sulphuric acid for about one minute.   This has the effect
of converting any non-reducing sugar into reducing sugar.   Hence,
if the acid is neutralised with ammonia, the solution can be boiled
with Fehling's solution.   A red precipitate now shows that non-
reducing sugar was originally present.

If both reducing and non-reducing sugars are present the non-
reducing sugar must be removed first.   This can be done by
boiling the solution of sugars in a conical flask or porcelain basin
and running in Fehling's solution from a burette.   At first the
blue colour of the Fehling's will be discharged and replaced by
the orange or red colour of cuprous oxide.   Ultimately the blue
colour of the Fehling's will no longer be discharged.   That means
that there is no more reducing sugar in solution.   Now filter the
solution and test it for non-reducing sugar as described above.

Remember that Fehling's solution is both *poisonous* and *caustic*
(it will burn your skin or holes into your clothes).   It requires
careful handling.

which just twine round and develop woody tissue to keep themselves in place. The honeysuckle (*Lonicera periclymenum*), larger bindweed (*Calystegia sepium*) which you may know as convolvulus, black bryony (*Tamus communis*) are examples, as is the runner bean of our gardens. Some of these plants twine in a clockwise manner, others in a counter-clockwise direction. To find out which way a particular plant twines, imagine yourself at the apex of the plant looking down onto the ground where a clock, face up, is ticking away. The direction the hands move is said to be clockwise. If the spiral which your twining plant has made goes in the other direction, then it is counter-clockwise.

However, it is not with the direction of climb that I am concerned here, but with two other features of climbing. Firstly, what is the least angle the support must make with the ground if the climber is to twine round it; and secondly, how thick must the support be in order to enable the plant to twine? If you have a little piece of garden available it is easy to find the answer to both these questions.

To find the angle of climb

I have experimented with both the scarlet runner and the bindweed. Perhaps you will be able to obtain the bean plants easier than bindweed. On a piece of recently-dug ground erect a vertical pole 6 to 8 ft. high and tie onto it *very firmly* several thick garden canes which will be perhaps 6 ft. long. The canes should be driven into the ground something after the fashion of the poles of a teepee tent (Fig. 31) but in such a manner that they make different angles with the ground, say approximately 20°, 30°, 40°, 50°, 60° and 75°. It helps to keep the canes rigid if tied to nails driven beneath them into the pole. To establish the angles the canes make with the ground, you will need an assistant. First cut out from cardboard a number of right-

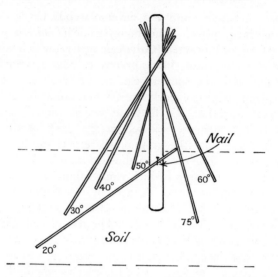

FIG. 31.—Arrangement of stout canes, 6 ft. long, around a central pole. The canes make differing angles with the ground, as shown.

angled triangles, each triangle carrying one of the other angles you require. A triangle need only be quite small, say 4 in. along the hypotenuse. Hold it between finger and thumb (see Fig. 32). Then, if you stand a few yards distant, and close one eye whilst you squint past the cardboard with the other, you can direct your assistant very accurately where to drive the first nail into the post. I do the cane making 20° with the ground first, as it is the lowest, and then carry on with the 30°, 40°, and so on to the 75° cane. You will see that the ground end of the 75° cane is much nearer to the pole than that of the 20° cane (Fig. 31).

In June sow three or four beans *beneath* each cane, and 3 in. nearer the post than the points where the canes enter the soil. All you have to do now is wait until the beans have germinated and the plants begin to twine up their canes, or not to twine, as the case may be. From this experiment, however, you can expect only an approximate answer. Suppose the beans climb the 70° cane but not the 60° one nor any of the others with an angle of inclination to the ground less than 60°. It will be clear to you that the

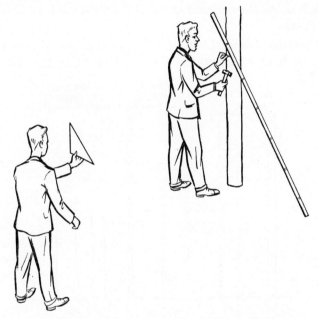

FIG. 32.—Establishing a particular pole with the chosen angle to the ground.

angle must be somewhere between 60° and 75°. To find this critical angle repeat the experiment but now have canes at 60°, 63°, 66°, 69,° 72° and 75°. You should obtain a much more accurate assessment of the critical angle of climb. I may say that I have taken the above values merely to explain the method, and give no guarantee that the angle for scarlet runner beans will be between 60° and 75°. You will, of course, readily see that results for one kind of plant cannot be applied to others. Each species has to be tested separately.

It is useful in slug-infested gardens to place a ring of lime round each group of seedlings.

To find out the thickness of the support acceptable to runner beans

Everyone knows that runner beans will climb up supports which have a diameter of $\frac{1}{2}$ in. to 1 in. Can they twine

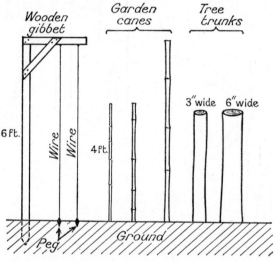

Fig. 33.—Apparatus to test which diameters of supports a plant can scale.

round very thin supports, or round very thick ones? This is easy to test if you can obtain a number of sticks varying from $\frac{1}{4}$ in. diameter to, say, 6 in. or more diameter. In an experiment I once performed, the beans certainly failed to climb a tree trunk which was about 1 ft. in diameter.

The best way to obtain supports less than $\frac{1}{4}$ in. is to use wire, thick fencing wire for one, and thin wire which you may sometimes find round parcels. The sticks should be arranged in a row, projecting vertically from the soil. The wires can be hung from a kind of gibbet (Fig. 33) and attached at the lower end to pegs driven firmly into the ground. Now plant three or four beans around each support and when they have germinated and produced young plants you will be able to see the range of diameters of supports up which the runner bean can climb. It would be interesting to see if these supports can still be climbed if they are inclined just above the critical angle.

INDEX